This is No. 101 of 4800 copies of a deluxe, limited edition of *The History of Methodist Hospital of Indiana, Inc.: A Mission of Compassionate Health Care* prepared for the friends of Methodist Hospital.

_____
President
Methodist Health Foundation

_____
President
Methodist Hospital of Indiana, Inc.

_____
Author

_____

To Correct an Error

This is to correct an error concerning the authorship of *The History of Methodist Hospital of Indiana, Inc.: A Mission of Compassionate Health Care*.

Sole author of this work is Edward A. Leary, well known for his books on Indianapolis and Indiana. Mr. Leary, a professional writer and instructor at Ball State University where he teaches writing broadcast and courses in film history, wrote the book under contract with Methodist Hospital.

Dr. Kenneth E. Reed, Chief Executive Officer Associate for Church Relations at Methodist Hospital, served as chief researcher and editor.

*Methodist Hospital is more
than a place of healing.
Methodist is a commitment
to provide the very best
in health care,
compassion in its delivery,
devotion to its patients
and dedication to the God
we serve.*

Frank P. Lloyd, M.D.
President, Methodist Hospital

The History of Methodist Hospital of Indiana Inc.

A Mission of
Compassionate Health Care

Kenneth E. Reed and Edward A. Leary

Methodist Health Foundation
Indianapolis, Indiana

The History of Methodist Hospital of Indiana Inc.

Published by
The Methodist Health Foundation
1812 N. Meridian Street
Indianapolis, Indiana

Please address all inquiries and information about this first edition or corrections and additions for future editions to: Kenneth E. Reed, CEO Associate for Church Relations, Methodist Hospital, 1604 N. Capitol Avenue, Indianapolis, IN 46202.

Library of Congress Cataloging in Publication Data:

Reed, Kenneth E., 1928-
    A Mission of Compassionate Health Care.

    Bibliography: p.
    Includes index.
    1. Methodist Hospital of Indiana—History.
2. Indianapolis (Ind.)—Hospitals—History.
I. Leary, Ed.   II. Title.
RA982.I42M477   1984   362.1'1'0977252   84-27177
ISBN 0-9603164-1-X

Cover Photo by Camera Associates Inc.
Designed by Patterson/Thomas Inc.
Printed by Hilltop Press Inc.

Contents

Methodist Hospital of Indiana, Inc. Mission Statement

Methodist Hospital of Indiana, Inc. is organized, and shall at all times be operated exclusively as a charitable and educational corporation to:

• Establish and maintain hospitals for the treatment of sick, wounded and injured persons without respect to creed, color, or nationality;

• Dispense relief and charity to the poor and destitute;

• Provide educational opportunities for allied health personnel, clergy and volunteers;

• Cooperate with other formal educational programs to conduct scientific research in the fields of medicine and hospitalization;

• Give opportunity for students of medicine and members of hospital medical staff to acquire further practical knowledge in the art and science of medicine;

All based upon the health and welfare heritage and the standards of accreditation promulgated by the United Methodist Church.

Article II
Articles of Acceptance of
Methodist Hospital of Indiana, Inc.

Revised and officially adopted
March 4, 1982

Preface

T he history of an institution provides a solid basis for appreciating its current work and understanding future decisions and actions.

This book explores the major accomplishments of Methodist Hospital during the 85 years since its founding. It also chronicles the story of Indianapolis and Indiana and the surrounding political environment.

It is more than the story of a hospital. It is also the story of people and the human spirit. Methodism's founder, John Wesley, believed that it was the duty of the Church to care for the whole person — to treat physical ills as well as souls. I believe this commitment to compassionate health care has been provided by dedicated and generous people from all walks of life. It was—and is—their interest, their love and their compassion that made this hospital great and enables us, in this our 85th year, to move ahead and dare to dream of new greatness and expanded vistas of service in the century ahead.

This book is their book. They made it possible.

Frank P. Lloyd, M.D.
President
Methodist Hospital of Indiana, Inc.
December, 1984

Foreword

T he word "Methodist" in the name of Methodist Hospital is much more than a title. It identifies a motivation for ministries of healing that adds to the techniques of medical care the dimension of concern for persons as children of God, created in the image of God with souls that inhabit bodies and, hence, make those bodies of special worth. The establishment of Methodist Hospital as recorded in this story was mandated by a commitment to continue the ministry of Jesus Christ who clearly indicated by His life and teachings that God is concerned about people as total persons. Reading the Gospels' account of Jesus' life makes one aware of how much His ministry dealt with the bodies of people as instruments through which the purposes of the spirit could be fulfilled. Across the centuries, those who have responded to His call have undertaken ways to continue His concern for physical health, recognizing that such concern was inseparably related to the well-being of the total life of persons. Development of health care through all the Christian centuries has been nourished again and again by the commitment of the Christian community throughout the world. The first instances of hospital care were under Christian auspices. St. Basil the Great of Caesarea (330-379 A.D.) developed a carefully planned system to aid persons in need which included a hospital, facilities for the ambulatory, the crippled, the orphans and foundlings, a separate building for lepers, living quarters for the staff and rooms for travelers. Guides were sent out to find the persons in need and bring them to the Xenodocheum.

When John Wesley started the Methodist movement, he insisted on including attention to physical needs as a part of the ministries his followers sponsored. He established what would now be called "out-patient clinics" for the treatment of people for whom medical care in that day was inadequate, too expensive, if not unavailable.

Followers of John Wesley migrated from England to the Colonies of the New World and established "The Methodist Episcopal Church" in 1784. Almost from the beginning that new church expressed its concern for the establishment of institutions of education and healing wherever the westward movement of people in the New World established centers of population. In this regard, two structures had particular importance. One was the Protestant Deaconess Movement in Europe which was integrated into the structure of the Methodist Episcopal Church. Young women were recruited as deaconesses in the new church with special responsibilities in relationship to education, health care and community service. That structure continues to this day in the organization of the United Methodist Church. The youth of the new church were gathered into societies and later called "Epworth League", named after the village in England where John Wesley grew up. This organization of youth, which has now become the United Methodist Youth Fellowship, also became actively involved in the educational and healing ministries of the Church. This story reveals the special relationship of the Epworth League program to establishment of Methodist Hospital of Indiana, Inc. Both the educational and healing institutions established by the Methodist Episcopal Church were always inclusive—for everyone, and not just for Methodists. They became community services for which the Methodist Church had a particular concern. There has been a responsible relationship of the people in Indiana called Methodists to the growth and development of Methodist Hospital of which the City of Indianapolis is justifiably proud.

Although members and officials of the United Methodist Church continue to be related to the operation and management of Methodist Hospital, it properly belongs to the whole community. The relationship of the word "Methodist" in its title is not one of ownership or control but of spirit. It means that basic to the purpose of the ministries provided is a Christian concern for the total life of persons for whom physical health is a significant factor. It is the inherent spirit of this ministry that patients in our hospital are never simply medical cases but human representatives of a divine reality. The processes of life from birth through death are cared for with an awareness that our bodies are the instruments of a spirit that gives life meaning and eternal value.

I commend to your reading this story of one very significant expression of Christian concern for persons for which the United Methodist Church and its predecessors have sought to be responsible agents.

Ralph T. Alton, Bishop
Indiana Area
United Methodist Church

Chapter One

A Convention Surplus

Do all the good you can,
By all the means you can,
In all the ways you can,
In all the places you can,
At all the times you can,
To all the people you can
As long as ever you can.
—John Wesley (1703-1791)
Rules of Conduct

There's not an automobile in sight in this turn-of-the-century photograph taken at the busy intersection of Washington and Illinois Streets, Indianapolis. It is the age of the horse and wagon, the bicycle, the streetcar, long skirts, high button shoes, dollar watches, dime novels and patent medicines. It is also a time when hospitals are coming into their own thanks to new advances in medicine and acceptance of the germ theory of infection.

July of 1899 was a busy month in Indianapolis. Besides the city's gala Fourth of July celebration, there were bicycle races at the Newby Oval, 30th and Central Avenue, and other races at the Broad Ripple Track where a soft-spoken black man, Marshall Major Taylor, was setting new records and pedaling his way to a world's championship. On July 19, the Forepaugh-Sells Consolidated Circus came to town, staged a "mammoth mile long street parade" and played to capacity crowds at the "old circus grounds" on East Washington Street. And for four days, from Thursday, July 20, to Sunday, July 23, the city played host to the year's largest convention—the fourth annual International Convention of the Epworth League of the Methodist Episcopal Church.

The Epworth League Convention was a special event. For months the city's seven newspapers, including two printed in German, had been filled with stories of the intensive preparations to house, feed and entertain the more than 10,000 delegates. *The Indianapolis News* reported that some 3,000 local homes were being thrown open to house the conventioneers and all of the city's Protestant churches had joined to provide headquarters for delegates from the various states, Alaska, and the British possessions. The Commercial Club, forerunner of the Indianapolis Chamber of Commerce, purchased a large tent, costing $1,200, which would seat several thousand delegates. The white tent with its broad blue stripes was erected on the grounds of the Marion County Courthouse.

The Commercial Club and Indianapolis citizens, churches, businesses and industries contributed funds toward a $9,000 goal to defray the costs of the convention. Additional funds came from the

For the 1899 Epworth League Convention, this large tent was erected on the lawn of the Marion County Courthouse. Purchased by the Indianapolis Commercial Club, it cost $1,200 and seated several thousand delegates. (Indianapolis Star photograph.)

sale of souvenir programs and song books for 25-cents each and a 25-cents admission charge to a band concert and songfest at the Indiana State Fairgrounds.

The news that 1,200 to 1,500 young black men and women were to attend the convention evoked some open and ugly racist comments. These were quickly squelched, however, by Edward L. Gilliam, vice chairman of arrangements, in a letter to *The Indianapolis News*. Writing in a day when segregation was a way of life (in Indianapolis there were even separate bicycle races for white and "colored" cyclists), Mr. Gilliam struck an early blow for civil rights. "There was no plan," he wrote, "to segregate the blacks attending the convention and the Negro delegates will come and go as they please and sit where they please, just as the other delegates will."

The city's newspapers also explained to their readers that the Epworth League was the official young people's organization of the Methodist Episcopal Church and represented the consolida-

tion of five different young people's societies of the Methodist Episcopal Church. The youth league, which had organized in 1889 at Cleveland, Ohio, adopted its name from the English town of Epworth, birthplace of the father and organizer of Methodism, John Wesley. The colors of one of the youth groups, a white ribbon with a scarlet thread running through it, were adopted as the official colors of the new Epworth League. For an emblem, a Maltese Cross was adopted and across it was written the League's motto, "Look Up, Lift Up."

During the ensuing years, the Indiana Epworth League grew in number and service. In 1896 the League counted 17,428 members enrolled in 342 chapters in nine different districts of the Indiana Conference of Methodists. To strengthen the league program, churches were urged to start Junior Leagues of boys and girls between 13 and 18 years of age. Moores Hill College (now the University of Evansville) and DePauw University, both supported by the Methodist Episcopal Church, were schools of higher learning recommended to Methodist youth.

It was appropriate that Indianapolis should be selected for the Epworth League Convention. Indianapolis and Indiana had long been a Meth-

HEADQUARTERS EPWORTH LEAGUE.

The Denison Hotel

Indianapolis, Ind.

T J. CULLEN.
Manager.

A STRICTLY FIRST-CLASS HOTEL of four hundred guests' rooms.

Advertisement for the Denison Hotel in the Epworth League Souvenir Book and Official Programme. The 400-room Denison stood on the southeast corner of Pennsylvania and Ohio Streets. James Whitcomb Riley, the poet, lived at the Denison before moving to Lockerbie Street.

odist stronghold and, in fact, the first sermon ever preached in the town, in 1819, had been given by a Methodist, the Reverend Resen Hammond, who held services under a walnut tree near the present site of the State Capitol. He had been followed by the Reverend William Cravens, a circuit rider for the Missouri Conference of Methodists, whom contemporary writers described as a huge man of some 300 pounds who often preached sitting in a cane-backed chair. The Reverend Cravens organized the Indiana District of the Methodist Episcopal Church and, at a meeting in Isaac Wilson's log cabin, located on the northwest corner of State House Square, organized the city's first Methodist Church. In 1825 the Methodists rented a hewed log cabin on the south side of Maryland Street and worshipped there until 1829 when they moved to a new brick church, which they named Wesley Chapel, on the southwest corner of the Circle and Meridian Streets. Later, in 1842, Wesley Chapel was divided into two charges (churches): Wesley Chapel, which remained on the Circle to serve all persons living west of Meridian Street, and Roberts Chapel (Park) which was to serve all persons east of Meridian Street. Built in 1843-44 on the corner of Market and Pennsylvania Streets, Roberts Park boasted Indianapolis' first town clock which was set in the square base of the spire. The church bell also served the downtown area as a fire alarm.

Both churches moved into new buildings in 1870. Wesley Chapel moved to the southwest corner of New York and Meridian Streets and changed its name to Meridian Street Methodist Episcopal Church. Roberts Park built one of the most imposing churches in the city on the northeast corner of Delaware and Vermont Streets, modeled after the Romanesque architecture of City Temple in London. Roberts Park was selected as a headquarters for the Epworth League Convention as well as the 400-room (200 with bath) Denison Hotel at the corner of Pennsylvania and Ohio Streets.

In 1899 there were 42 Indianapolis Methodist Churches (nine black and 33 white), each with its own Epworth League whose young members joined with others from around the state to greet the arriving convention delegates at the busy Union Station. Wearing white caps, the Indiana Leaguers escorted the visitors through bunting draped streets to the State House where the delegates were registered and escorted to their hotels, boarding houses or temporary homes. Many of the early arrivals took the opportunity to tour the busy, bustling, prosperous city of 169,164 people, which was both a major manufacturing as well as a railroad center.

Among the downtown sights were the City Market adjoining Tomlinson Hall and the magnificent English Hotel and Opera House curving gracefully with the Circle where, behind a high wooden fence plastered with bill posters, workmen were busy erecting the city's most famous landmark—the Soldiers and Sailors Monument.

Official badge worn by the more than 10,000 delegates attending the 1899 Epworth League International Convention at Indianapolis. The League represented the consolidation of five different youth groups of the Wesleyan movement. Its motto was "Look Up, Lift Up."

Downtown traffic was a mad mix of street cars including the so-called "open" or summer trolleys, bicycles, and horse drawn vehicles that included buggies, drays, hacks and surreys. Automobiles in 1899 were still a novelty and there were perhaps fewer than a dozen in the city although Waverly and National had begun to manufacture their first cars. There were also stores to be visited such as H.P. Wasson, L.S. Ayres, Charlie Mayers, George J. Marrott's Shoe Store and the When Department Store, which gave every boy a baseball bat with the purchase of a suit.

The Epworth League Convention proved to be a great success. The thousands of young people who attended heard discussions by prominent youth leaders on such subjects as "How to Help Revivals," "Epworth Houses and Work in the Cities," "The League and Its Members," and "The League and the Strangers." Outstanding speakers lectured on "Abraham Lincoln," "The Last Days of the Confederacy," "Methodism: Its Life and Spirit," "Missions," and "Temperance." Special attention was given to congregational singing and hymns were sung at every session, many of them from the pens of John Wesley and his brother, Charles, famous as a hymnist and the author of some 6,500 hymns. Virtually all of the city's Protestant churches were used for the various meetings and services in addition to the 5,000-seat Tomlinson Hall and the big tent on the courthouse lawn.

There was also time for fun in the form of chaperoned porch parties, bicycle tours and moonlight trolley rides. At the State Fairgrounds, Y.M.C.A. athletic teams delighted crowds with a Pentathlon Exhibition that consisted of a 100-yard dash, one mile run, pole vaulting, high jumping and hammer throwing. Three bicycle races were staged for the one, two and five-mile state championships. That same night an Indianapolis band and a massed chorus, representing the best voices from the city's many church choirs, gave a concert in front of the Fairgrounds grandstand.

Meeting at the Roberts Park Methodist Church a few days after the convention, the committee in charge composed of the Reverend Charles Lasby, Reverend W.A. Quayle, W.T. Malott, O.H. Palmer and W.C. Van Arsdel agreed that the convention had been a success on all counts. Attendance had exceeded expectations, the city's response had been open hearted and generous, and

Reverend Edward B. Rawls   Reverend George M. Smith   Reverend Leslie J. Naftzger

Three men who played significant roles in helping make Methodist Hospital a reality. The Reverend Edward B. Rawls, presiding elder of the Indianapolis District, presented the proposal and resolution to build a Methodist Hospital at Indianapolis to the Indiana Conference of the Methodist Episcopal Church. And it was the Reverend George M. Smith of Indianapolis whose stirring speech turned the tide at the Conference in favor of the project. The Reverend Leslie J. Naftzger of Muncie was elected the first president of the Methodist Hospital Board of Trustees. The Reverend Smith would later serve as superintendent of the hospital.

the programs well received. In addition, the convention had been a financial success. In fact, after all the bills were paid, there remained the sum of $4,750 in the convention fund, a substantial amount in a day of uninflated dollars. The committee discussed at length the many possibilities of using the surplus for a good Christian cause. Finally, at the suggestion of the Reverend Lasby, pastor of the Central Avenue Methodist Church, the committee voted to donate the money toward the start of a building fund for the construction of a Methodist hospital in Indianapolis. Dr. Lasby had been associated with the founding of the first Methodist hospital in the United States, in Brooklyn, New York, which may have provided some basis for his suggestion.

The proposal, however, required the approval of the Indiana Conference of the Methodist Episcopal Church and the Reverend Edward B. Rawls, presiding elder of the Indianapolis District, was appointed to prepare and present a resolution at the annual meeting of the conference to be held in Greencastle on September 13.

Indications were that the conference would look favorably upon the Indianapolis proposal. The conference had already shown its interest in medicine and hospitals dating back to 1849, when, in cooperation with the Methodist sponsored Asbury College (later DePauw University), it established Indiana Central Medical College in Indianapolis. The college, located on the third floor of the Johnson Building on Washington Street, between Meridian and Pennsylvania Streets, offered a modern curriculum and, for the times, a highly qualified faculty. More than 100 students attended the school during its three years of operation. Financial difficulties forced its closing in 1852.

With the reuniting of the Indiana and Southeast Conferences in 1895, the Elizabeth Gamble Deaconess Home and Christ Hospital in Cincinnati, Ohio, and Deaconess Hospital, Jeffersonville (now Clark County Hospital), came under the influence of the Indiana Conference. Two Indiana citizens, Dr. J.H. Wynn, Indianapolis, and Dr. C.E. Bacon, Evansville, served as trustees and, on the second Sunday of each October, collections were taken up in Methodist churches to support the hospitals.

In 1898 the conference had also taken another

important step which presaged well for the Indianapolis proposal. Some members of the conference had suggested that a Methodist Hospital be established in Indiana and, as a result, a committee was named consisting of the Reverends F. S. Tincher, George H. Murphy and J. Wesley Maxwell, to conduct a feasibility study. Their report had been favorable and Articles of Association were drawn up and adopted. No action, however, was taken to appropriate funds or to make plans for construction.

It was against this backdrop that the Reverend Rawls presented his proposal and resolution at the Annual Conference in Greencastle. A contemporary writer has left us this description of what transpired:

"Dr. Rawls arose in the meeting to read the resolution and moved its adoption. The conference was stunned! One of the members of the conference, Dr. B. F. Rollins, a man of prestige with a dynamic personality and big voice, spoke out, 'Brethren, we have all we can carry on our Church. Now you have come to put upon it one million dollars. Great God, men, where are we going to stop? I am opposed to this hospital proposition.'

"A young preacher, the Reverend George M. Smith, who had never before risen to address the conference, was immediately on his feet. 'Men,' he said, 'in reply to this brother's question as to where are we going to stop, if I understand our Methodist Episcopal Church, it is not looking for a place to stop. The Church does not dare stop until it encompasses all the interests of Jesus Christ and our Church can never encompass all His interests and leave out sick people.'" Young Smith apparently hit the right note for the writer adds: "Reverend Smith's brave outburst turned the tide of opinion in favor of the project."

Adoption of the Articles of Association was voted by the conference and the new institution was named the Methodist Episcopal Hospital and Deaconess Home of the State of Indiana with the declared objective "to establish and maintain a hospital or hospitals for the treatment of the sick, wounded and injured persons, to dispense charity to the poor, and to establish and maintain a Deaconess Home or other kindred institutions." The Conference also voted to continue its support of Christ Hospital in Cincinnati and Jeffersonville Deaconess Hospital until "the Indiana hospital could be made ready for operation."

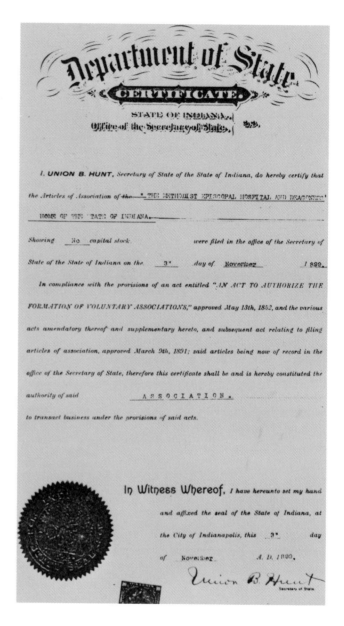

Following the filing of articles of association, the Indiana Secretary of State issued the above certificate authorizing The Methodist Episcopal Hospital and Deaconess Home of the State of Indiana to transact business. The certificate is dated November 3, 1899.

No time was lost in organizing and planning for the new hospital. Articles of Incorporation were filed with the Secretary of State, directors appointed, and the first board meeting was held on October 10, 1899 at the Meridian Street Methodist Church. A month later the directors, elected by the Northwest, North and Indiana Conferences of the Methodist Episcopal Church, became the Board of Trustees. The first Board members were: *From the Indiana Conference:* The Reverend Dr. Rawls; the Reverend W.C. Van Arsdel; Mrs. H. Schmidlap; the Reverend George M. Smith, Indianapolis; Mrs.

A.V.P. Adams, Shelbyville. *From the Northwest Conference:* H.N. Ogden, Covington; Dr. Oliver Card, Frankfort; D.M. Wood, Lebanon; Mrs. W.C. Woods, Terre Haute. *From the North Indiana Conference:* B.A. Kemp, Elkhart; C.C. Binkley, Richmond; the Reverend Leslie J. Naftzger, Muncie; Mrs. Emma L. Daniel, Decatur; Mrs. L.H. Bunyan, Richmond.

The Board elected the Reverend Leslie J. Naftzger president and Reverend George M. Smith, secretary. With organization complete, the Board made plans for acquiring a site for the proposed hospital.

In 1899 Indianapolis had three hospitals, each overcrowded and forced to turn patients away. Newest of the three hospitals was the Protestant Deaconess Hospital and Home for the Aged at 200 North Senate, which opened in 1895 with the Reverend J.C. Peters as superintendent. His tenure was apparently brief for the city directory of 1900 lists the head of the hospital as Sister Minnie Maman, Matron. Most of the Protestant churches were affiliated with the hospital and participated in its operation. The hospital's name, Deaconess, was derived from the Protestant sisterhood that founded and operated the institution. Deaconesses were a group of dedicated women, at least 21 years of age, licensed and consecrated by the church, who had given themselves "wholly to Christian work among those who need them most." Dressed modestly in long black dresses with white collars or ties and turned over white cuffs, deaconesses were also deemed to be modest in their needs for they were provided with "moderate keep" and $2 a week. "She is expected," according to one writer, "to go where she is sent and count not her life dear unto her. She is often put under the press of the most taxing toil. She is to know what it is to be weary."

The other of the newer hospitals was the 40-bed St. Vincent Hospital at South and Delaware, where it had moved in 1889 from its original location on East Vermont Street. The first of the city's Catholic hospitals, it was opened in 1881 by four Sisters of the Daughters of Charity of St. Vincent de Paul at the specific request of Bishop Chatard. Sister Mary Theresa, one of the four founding nuns, was the hospital's first superintendent.

Oldest of the three Indianapolis hospitals was City Hospital (now Wishard Memorial) which was municipally owned and operated. Its long and often controversial history reflected the changing views of the average citizen toward hospitals and hospital care.

When Indianapolis was still in its pioneer phase, hospitals were looked upon as "pest houses" and associated with poverty and poor houses or places of last refuge where those suffering from contagious diseases, an incurable complaint or senility were committed to spend their last days. Few of the early movers and shakers saw the need for a hospital and it was only when epidemics struck that there was talk of building a hospital. A case in point was the possibility of an outbreak of cholera in 1849-50. A movement was immediately launched to build a hospital, but as the threat of an epidemic passed, the plans were just as speedily dropped.

An outbreak of smallpox in 1855 created a new panic among the townspeople and demands were renewed for a hospital where patients could be sent and separated from the rest of the population. The City Council, under the urging of two of the city's leading pioneer doctors, Dr. John S. Bobbs and Dr. Livingston Dunlap, ordered the construction of a hospital. Choosing a site, however, proved difficult. Everyone was in favor of building a hospital, but no one, it seemed, wanted the "pest house" built in his area. People talked about the possibility of contagion, bad smells, and the effect on property values. One man writing to a local newspaper expressed fear that the screams of the patients might keep his neighbors awake.

At long last, however, lots were purchased in a large, open wasteland surrounded by swamps at the extreme northwestern corner of the city near the point where Crawfordsville Road crosses Fall Creek. The land was cleared but construction had no sooner begun than the smallpox scare subsided. As a consequence the work languished, annual appropriations were reduced, and it was not until four years later, in 1859, that the hospital was finished. As far as the townspeople were concerned, there was no longer any need for a hospital. The building remained empty and unused, except for a brief period when it was used as a House of Refuge for Friendless Women, a 19th century euphemism for prostitutes.

With the outbreak of the Civil War, the city government turned the City Hospital over to the U.S. Government which converted it into a military hospital. After the war ended in 1865 the hospital was closed, used briefly as a soldier's home, and returned to the city greatly enlarged and improved. In the spring of 1866 the city purchased furniture and supplies at sales of surplus government property at Jeffersonville and established a city hospital with an appropriation of $6,000 a year for its operation.

Thurman R. Rice, M.D., in his *One Hundred Years Of Medicine* gives us a picture of the early City Hospital and its problems. He writes: "The superintendent chosen (to run the hospital) was Dr. Greenly V. Woollen. The honor was a dubious one. For several years after Woollen, the superintendency changed every year—nor was it an example of a political plum being passed from one faithful politician to another. On the contrary, the appointment was dreaded, but the physicians knew that someone had to take the job and so they passed the duty from one physician to the next....Somewhat later when more surgery was being done, it was said to be possible to find the place (the hospital) even on the darkest night if one followed his nose—the stench arising from the wards with suppurating wounds, or later the odor of iodoform, was that strong. The townspeople of 1870 never went near the place if it were possible to avoid it; the hospital and horrible dump which had been made of the grounds where the Medical Center is now located, were the heartbreaking problem of one city administration after another for decades."

By the turn of the century, the public attitude toward hospitals had undergone a tremendous change. Hospitals were no longer looked upon as a place of last resort, but a place to get well. This new outlook, born in an age of social concern and religious activism, ushered in an era of hospital construction in virtually every major U.S. city and, in fact, more than half of America's hospitals would be founded in the first decade of the new century.

An Indianapolis physician, Dr. Frank B. Wynn, writing for a Methodist publication in 1900, described the change this way: "The evolution of the hospital as a habitation where the sick may acquire the most perfect care, medical and otherwise, is a modern development. The growth of the hospital is partly due to the impulse of charity and partly due to discoveries...in the fields of bacteriology. As the result of these discoveries, surgeons and physicians have found the best possi-

ble ends in treatment are secured in a hospital."

Public attitudes toward the practice of medicine were also undergoing a change. The 19th century had been the era of the purgers, the bleeders, the botanicals and the eclectics, but it had also marked the discovery of the germ theory, improved sanitation, and the development of such new instruments as the stethoscope, the microscope and the sphygmomanometer. For the first time scientific thought, practical achievements in technology and science, and social factors, were linked in the fight against disease. All this was in sharp contrast to earlier days when most families relied on home remedies, patent medicines, "granny women" and ill equipped, poorly trained, but well meaning doctors. Max Adeler, a 19th century humorist, best illustrates how patients were treated in an earlier day by the different types of practicing physicians:

> Four doctors tackled Johnny Smith
> They blistered and they bled him;
> With squills and anti-bilious pills
> And ipecac, they fed him.
> They stirred him up with calomel,
> And tried to move his liver;
> But all in vain—his little soul
> Was wafted o'er The River.

The failure of the doctors or the death of Johnny Smith was not an isolated case. The story is told of a doctor in one Indiana town who, during a cholera epidemic, ordered medicine for the patient "to be given every hour on the hour until he dies." This was probably as good advice as he could provide.

Death was a regular visitor to every 19th century family. Few family circles were unbroken. Deaths among babies were so common that mothers breathed a sigh of relief when they brought a child through a second summer. Most people in those earlier times died of the so-called "wasting diseases" such as smallpox, cholera, typhoid, malaria and the measles; few lived long enough to develop the degenerative diseases of heart, liver and kidneys. At the turn of the century average life expectancy was 47 years; in pioneer days even less.

Louis Pasteur's discovery, in 1862, of the germ theory of infection had been the turning point in medicine. Now, for the first time, diseases could be defined bacteriologically. Not everyone, however, was willing to accept Pasteur's theory, particularly medical scientists with antiontological tendencies.

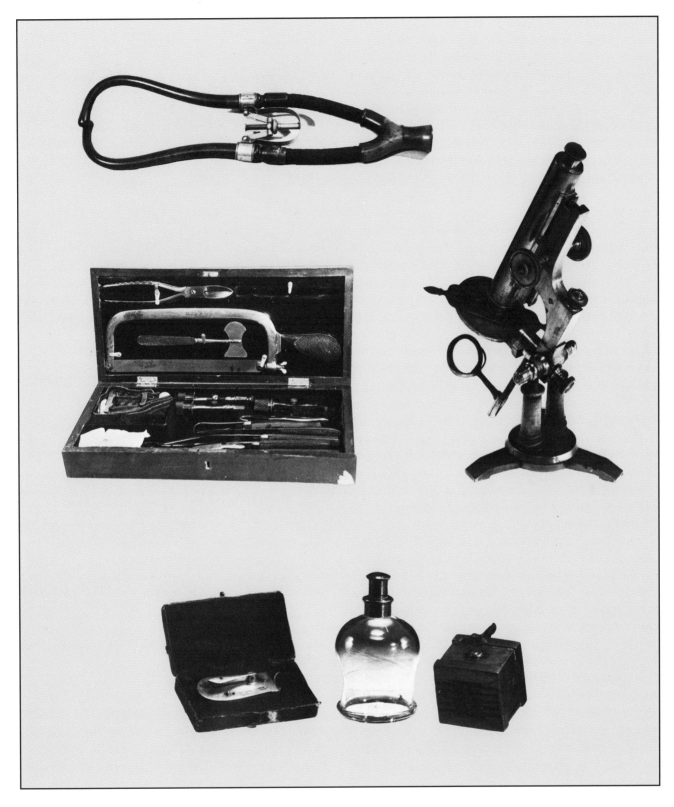

Nineteenth century medical instruments included a binaural stethoscope, an amputation kit, an early version of the microscope and bloodletting devices used in an age when bleeding was presumed to purify the blood. Shown above, left to right, are a spring lancet, cupping glass and brass scarificator, the latter a small brass box, about two inches square, with hidden cutting edges or small sharp knives released by a trigger to produce lacerations in the skin. Glass cups were then placed over the area to draw the blood. Some physicians used bloodletting for almost every ailment and advocated patients be bled until unconscious. Leeches were also used to suck poisoned blood from the patient. (Indiana Medical History Museum.)

In Indiana, for instance, as late as 1881, the president of the State Medical Society was quoted as observing that "the germ theory is still problematic." The following year Robert Koch not only provided the theory's most important confirmation, but its most decisive victory — the discovery of tubercle baccilus.

By 1900, however, the germ theory had gained general acceptance and bacteriology became a new science along with a new lay and professional regard for scientific methods of diagnosis and treatment. Aseptic and antiseptic surgery became common. Cholera and typhoid fever were stamped out with improved sanitation. The draining of swamps brought about the destruction of the malaria carrying mosquito. Although anti-vaccination societies flourished and even many doctors opposed the idea, more people than ever were vaccinated against smallpox. The formation of state boards of health and county health boards gave added impetus to a movement to improved sanitation and the health of its citizens. In 1881, Dr. Thaddeus M. Stevens, a graduate of Central Indiana Medical College, became the first secretary and executive officer of the Indiana State Board of Health. State boards of examination and registration were established in an effort to weed out medical quacks—particularly botanicals and eclectics—and to set new, high standards for the medical profession.

Indicative of the need for professional standards was an Indiana survey of 1883 that counted 5,376 doctors in the state, of which 2,056 were not graduates of any school and 48 could not even write their names. More evidence was provided in the first annual report of Indiana's State Board of Medical Examination filed in 1898. The State Medical Society, which had earlier criticized the law creating the Board calling it "a compromise affair with low standards," reported to its members that of the 4,000 licensed doctors listed in the report, 600 were "mountebanks," doctors who hawked medicines of doubtful value door to door, by mail, and from the tailgate of wagons in the town square.

It was also the era of the patent medicine and thousands of Indianians in common with other gullible Americans purchased and used vast quantities of these cure-alls in the form of liquids, pills, tablets, liver pads and electric belts. Testimonials and advertisements frequently promised these

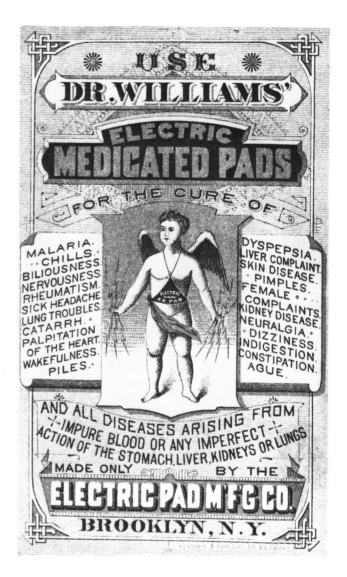

Typical patent medicine trade card at the turn of the century. The basic ingredient in Dr. Williams' electric medicated pad was capsicum - red pepper. Customers placed a red spot on the pad directly over the liver and as the mixture of red pepper and glue melted at body temperature it spread a warm "health-giving" glow over the afflicted area. (Bella C. Landauer Collection, New York Historical Society, New York City.)

nostrums would do "more good than a doctor." Among the most popular of the patented nostrums that could be purchased from the medicine men as well as at the corner drug store were: Wa-hoo Bitters, Kickapoo Indian Oil, Hamlon's Wizard Oil, Lydia Pinkham's Vegetable compound (for ladies' complaints) and Dr. Thomas's Electric Oil. Typical of the patent medicine promises was that of a Kickapoo Indian remedy, Sagwa, which its promoters said would cure constipation, liver complaint, dyspepsia, indigestion, rheumatism, chills and fevers or "any diseases arising from impure blood of the deranged liver." Many of the patent medicines listed their dosage as "one for a man, two for a horse."

One of the most popular medicine shows in Indiana was that of "Doc" C.M. Townsend who numbered among his company the future poet, James Whitcomb Riley, who played a bass drum and illustrated Doc Townsend's lectures on a blackboard. The Townsend company, which traveled all over Indiana and Ohio, sold Townsend's Wizard Oil and other patent medicines bottled under the doctor's personal label.

The newly formed county and state medical groups crusaded against these patent medicines as well as quack doctors. The American Medical Association published a 700-page book, *Nostrums and Quackery* in which it exposed the charlatans and mountebanks and pointed out the dangers inherent in the patent medicines which often had alcohol or opium as their base (apparently on the premise that if you couldn't cure the patient at least you could make him or her feel good.) The crusade was given added impetus by another popular book, *The Great American Fraud*, by Samuel Hopkins Adams. The book, which further exposed the patent medicines and their merchants, consisted of a collection of startling revelations he had earlier written for *Collier's* Magazine.

But all these problems seemed to fade in the excitement of welcoming in the new century. For those dedicated to medicine and those planning to build a Methodist hospital, there was only renewed hope and an unlimited future. There were those who talked about new horizons in health care, but no one could foretell the amazing transformation in medicine that would take place in the next several decades. Who among the young Epworth Leaguers, concerned clergy and laity voting to build a hospital in the year 1899, could foresee that doctors would one day, within its confines transplant a human heart?

Chapter Two

Building a Hospital

A man was going down from Jerusalem to Jericho, and he fell among robbers, who stripped him and beat him, and departed, leaving him half dead . . . A Samaritan . . . came to where he was; and when he saw him, he had compassion, and went to him and bound up his wounds, pouring on oil and wine; then he sat him on his own beast and brought him to an inn, and took care of him.

—Jesus' Parable of The Good Samaritan

Everybody wore a hat and milady's skirts swept the ground in 1905 when the cornerstone was laid for the new Methodist Hospital on October 25. Indiana Governor J. Frank Hanley officiated assisted by the Rev. C. Earle Bacon, president of the Board of Trustees; Rev. Leslie J. Natfzger, vice-president; Hiram W. Kellogg and W.P. McKinsey. Rev. C.N. Sims, Liberty, Ind., presided.

Meeting on December 4, 1899, the Methodist Hospital Board of Trustees took two important steps: it approved a site for the proposed hospital and appointed a committee to formulate plans for raising money and subscriptions.

The site selected—on the northwest corner of Illinois and 29th Streets—was in accordance with the expressed desire of the trustees that the hospital be located outside the mile square, apparently on the assumption that the new hospital would thus be located in an area destined for future growth. The price for the land, which included 150 feet on Kenwood Avenue, was $7,000.

Announcement of the site selection brought a flood of protests, most of them from the city's doctors whose offices were generally located in downtown Indianapolis. The doctors charged the site was "out of the way" and "inconvenient to get to." Besides, it was argued, downtown Indianapolis was *the* center of things—an argument not without its own logic in those turn-of-the-century days when most businesses, amusements, markets and residences were concentrated in the original mile square. The trustees, however, stuck to their guns and bravely defended their choice—at least for several months. Eventually, they reconsidered their action and decided to quietly seek out a new location closer to or in the downtown area.

Raising funds was also a problem. Despite yeoman efforts by the Board's fund raising committee, money and subscriptions came in slowly. Deciding that what was needed was a full-time, paid fund raiser, the board on April 1, 1901, employed the Reverend Dr. W.R. Halstead, of Frankfort, for $2,500 a year plus railroad fare and hotel expenses. At the time Dr. Halstead was hired, subscriptions "secured and in prospect"

After a site at the corner of Illinois and 29th Streets ran into opposition, Methodist Hospital's Board of Trustees purchased the present site at 16th Street and Capitol Avenue for $20,000. A former baseball park, the grounds are shown here in a 1902 photograph.

totaled $7,384 of the $200,000 needed.

The Reverend Halstead proved to be an indefatigable worker. As corresponding secretary, he wrote letters, sent telegrams, traveled all over the state. He visited Methodist churches to arrange for "Hospital Sundays" and he spoke before clubs, church groups and other organizations on the need for the hospital and the urgency of the cause. He also visited Epworth Leagues and the District Home Missionary Societies to spur them on to greater efforts.

As part of the fund raising activity, a four-page monthly magazine, *The Good Samaritan* was launched under the direction of the Board of Trustees with the Reverend Arthur H. Delong and the Reverend Joseph L. Stout as editor and publisher. The subscription price was 50 cents a year, but copies were free to those who contributed to the Methodist Hospital fund. Besides urging readers' gifts, the magazine, whose circula-

tion would eventually reach 20,000 copies, carried important news and statistics. It reported, for example, the endorsement of the Commerce Club of Indianapolis and members' comments on "the urgent need for larger (hospital) accommodations." It told its readers that, by careful estimate, 75 percent of the patients in Indianapolis' three hospitals were from outside the city and it reported, "there is room now in Indianapolis hospitals for only two of every four who apply for treatment." A later issue revised the figure to two out of every five.

When a gift and memorial building fund was established, *The Good Samaritan* listed those gifts which entitled the donor to an engraved silver tablet on the building or the donor's name on the door of the ward. Those who contributed one dollar had their names placed on a "long roll." The sums needed were not large by today's standards, but this was a time when families lived well on $400 a year. For instance, for $14,000 a donor could build and name a 16-bed ward or for $7,000 a children's ward of 12 cribs. A donor of $2,500 was privileged to name a room with two beds and for $1,500 a room with one bed. There were also endowments ranging from $250 to $5,000, the latter endowing a bed perpetually. For $1,500 a donor could maintain a bed for five years; $300 for a year. The small giver was not overlooked; $100, it was reported, would put 8,000 bricks in a wall and $15, 1,000 bricks. Bricks could also be purchased at 15 cents each.

Large donations to the building fund were slow in coming and the magazine editors were moved to lament on the lack of "princely gifts." It reported: "Some rich people have made liberal subscriptions, but very few. It is notorious that many of our rich stay home on Hospital Day." On the other hand, the magazine praised the generous contributions from "washerwomen and servants and the great masses of people." These contributions also included thousands of rolls of pennies donated by Sunday School children.

Meanwhile, the Board of Trustees settled on a new site for the hospital, a former baseball park at the corner of Capitol Avenue and 16th Street (then Tinker Street). Known as the Tinker Street Park, it was a former home of the Indianapolis Indians baseball team. The price was $14,000 and the purchase was negotiated for $3,000 down and a series of notes extending over four years with interest fixed at four and one-half percent semi-annually. To complete the tract, an additional piece of property at the northeast end of the proposed site (1632 Capitol Avenue) was purchased for $6,000. As for the former site at Illinois and 29th Street, it was disposed of at a modest profit, the reported sale price being $8,250.

Plans were also made for the building of the hospital. A building committee was named and the Indianapolis architectural firm of Vonnegut and Bohn was appointed to draw plans. The firm was one of the best in Indiana and Bernard Vonnegut, the senior partner, had designed the original L.S. Ayres & Company building, Das Deutsche Haus (later to be called the Athenaeum) and *The Indianapolis Star* building. Following a visit to public and private hospitals in Chicago, Cleveland, New York and Syracuse, N.Y., the Board decided to adopt the pavilion plan, one of three plans submitted by the architects. The plan provided for a series of five separate but connected buildings, generally conceded to be the best possible arrangement of wards, rooms and accessory buildings.

There was some grumbling among Methodists over the slowness of the hospital project and *The Good Samaritan* was quick to answer. "Funds to date," it reported in March, 1903, "have not justified letting the contract for the building." The magazine also defended the fund raising activity, pointing out that in 16 months, $50,000 had been raised, adding that "none of our Indianapolis churches have accumulated that much in their first 25 years."

By December of 1903 more than $94,000 had been raised of which $49,000 came from outside Indianapolis. This was about half the money needed for the hospital, and the trustees discussed the possibility of making a start, then decided against it. They were not going to give in to pressure; they were going to delay construction until additional money or the prospect of more funds was forthcoming. At the request of the Board, efforts were redoubled to raise the additional funds and *The Good Samaritan* responded with ringing editorials and an admonition: "O! Ye Methodists! March!"

In July of 1904 the Reverend Halstead, whose health had been ruined in his untiring efforts on behalf of the hospital, resigned. He was replaced as corresponding secretary by the Reverend C.N. Sims, D.D., a former president of Syracuse University, N.Y. Mrs. Lillian W. Gatch was named financial secretary.

In March of 1905 the Board of Trustees arrived at a momentous decision: to proceed at once with the construction of the administration building. Bids were called for and an Indianapolis contractor, George Weaver, was awarded the contract with the understanding the work was to be completed by January 1, 1906. Not all the funds had been subscribed for the complete hospital structure, but the prospects looked bright, and a line of bank credit was available if needed. Looking behind the decision, it is probable that the Board believed that the actual start of the work and the laying of the hospital cornerstone would spur contributions. Donors would no longer be asked to give to a dream, but to a reality taking shape on the corner of Capitol Avenue and 16th Street.

The laying of the cornerstone on October 25, 1905 was a gala occasion and two Indianapolis men, famous on the national scene, were among the speakers: Charles Warren Fairbanks, Vice President of the United States, under Theodore Roosevelt, and Albert J. Beveridge, U.S. Senator from Indiana, who had won fame and stirred international controversy with his speeches on America's Manifest Destiny. The cornerstone was laid by Indiana Governor J. Frank Hanley, assisted by the Reverend C. Earle Bacon, president of the Board of Trustees; Leslie J. Naftzger, vice president; Hiram W. Kellogg and Reverend W.P. McKinsey. Other speakers included the Reverend Edwin H. Hughes, president of DePauw University; the Reverend W.D. Parr, Kokomo, a member of the Board of Trustees; and Mrs. Jane Bancroft Robinson, Detroit, Michigan. The Reverend Dr. Charles N. Sims, general secretary, presided. Prayer was offered by the Reverend Joshua Stansfield and the benediction was pronounced by the Reverend Arthur H. Delong, all members of the Board of Trustees. Music was provided by the North Indiana Conference Quartet.

Participants in the ceremony also received a firsthand report on the construction of this first unit. Three stories high and completely fireproof, it was to have a frontage of 143 feet and 43 feet wide with a large wing extending west on the middle axis 87 feet by 45 feet. The building was to incorporate a high basement, partition walls of brick and tile, and a roof that would be all steel. Trustees boasted that not a single stick of wood was being used in the building's construction.

With construction of the first unit underway, the Board of Trustees decided to proceed with plans for completing the other hospital units. It was a calculated risk as the building fund was still short of its goal and, in fact, it would remain this way until within a year of the hospital's formal opening, when an intensive and last minute campaign was launched to raise $75,000 to keep expenditures in line with income. Among the efforts was a successful and highly profitable "tag day" in Indianapolis that became an annual event.

The 1907 Tag Day was preceded by a news story in *The Indianapolis News,* obviously concocted by the news staff and the ladies in charge. Carrying a curiosity exciting black headline, WOMEN AND MONEY CAUSE T. WADD TO FLEE, the story reported that local financial circles had been stirred by the disappearance of T. Wadd, described as one of the city's "eminent men of money." All that was known of T. Wadd's disappearance was that he had left the city sometime during the night on a train heading west. His family, in an interview with a *News* reporter, refused to talk or to admit that T. Wadd was missing. As far as Mrs. Wadd

U.S. Vice President Charles Warren Fairbanks of Indianapolis was the principal speaker at the laying of the cornerstone for Methodist Hospital, October 25, 1905. Fairbanks would later become president of the Board of Trustees and a generous contributor to the growing hospital.

was concerned, she expected her husband would be back in the city late that night or early the next day.

A clerk in T. Wadd's office, however, had a different view. "I believe—am almost positive—that I know the cause of his disappearance," the clerk said. "Tight Wadd left town to escape the women of the Methodist Episcopal Church! He was afraid of being tagged for Methodist Hospital."

Thus, the way was paved for the 200 ladies of the Women's Home Missionary Society, who invaded downtown Indianapolis the next day in long, full, sweeping skirts, shirtwaists, closely fitted jackets and plumed hats.

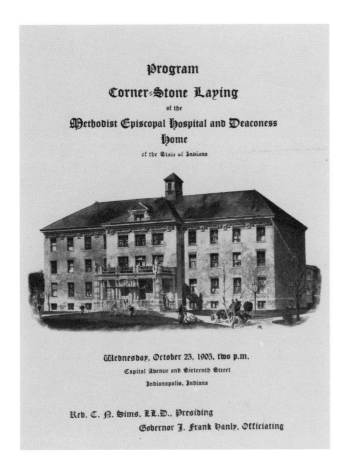

Program
Corner-Stone Laying
of the
Methodist Episcopal Hospital and Deaconess
Home
of the State of Indiana

Wednesday, October 25, 1905, two p.m.
Capitol Avenue and Sixteenth Street
Indianapolis, Indiana

Rev. C. A. Sims, LL.D., Presiding
Governor J. Frank Hanly, Officiating

Cover of the program for the laying of the cornerstone for the new Methodist Hospital, October 25, 1905. The picture is an artist's rendering of what the new hospital would look like when completed.

There were stories to be savored on that first Tag Day. The Reverend Dr. C.T. Alexander, an early historian of Methodist Hospital, related two of them in his unpublished manuscript. "Women of all creeds," he wrote, "were working beside these Methodist women as they have throughout the history of the hospital. A young woman from one of the Congregational Churches, who had gone out to sell tags, came back in a little while with thirty-seven dollars. 'Oh, we are all Methodists today,' she said."

Mrs. E.C. Tinsley of the Broadway Church had an unusual experience in the Newton-Claypool Building. As Alexander tells the story: "She had not been at work long when a new found friend presented her with a revolver—tied it around her neck, in fact—to guard the generous sums being handed her. Doctors and other professional men of the building got into the spirit and dropped money over the balconies in a reckless fashion."

Meanwhile construction of Methodist Hospital continued unabated with contributions sometimes matching need, but more often not. The Board of Trustees stood by their decision to complete the work. It was resolved that even if it were necessary to go into debt, the hospital would be finished and the various wards and rooms furnished. To avoid going into debt, a special campaign for a fund of $75,000 was announced in October of 1907. "Help more," was their plea. "We must have the money before opening day."

The board also announced that New Year's Day, 1908, would be Reception Day—a day for the public to visit and inspect the partially finished hospital. At the same time, plans were developed for the formal dedication and opening of the hospital in April.

On Reception Day, 5,000 Methodists and their friends converged on the unfinished hospital and, according to *The Good Samaritan*, "expressed their surprise and delight at the magnitude of the buildings and grounds as well as the pefect appointments of the hospital." Dr. William Wirt King was chairman of the Reception Day and, together with the Board of Trustees and a group of smooth functioning committees "was able to handle the crowds without confusion or difficulty. Refreshments were provided by the ladies organizations of the several Indianapolis Methodist Churches and the ladies of Hall Place Methodist Church served Sunday dinner for those who cared to patronize them."

Although Reception Day was an informal gathering and no concerted effort was made to obtain donations or subscriptions, the visitors subscribed about $3,500. Among the larger subscriptions was that of Mr. and Mrs. H.W. Miller of Indianapolis in the form of a deed for real estate valued at $2,000. Among the other donations were those of a group of Junior Epworth Leaguers who brought stockings filled with pennies. They were personally thanked by Governor Hanley, a member of the reception committee, and Lew Robertson, district president of the Epworth League. "It was," reported *The Good Samaritan*, "an impressive and touching part of the reception."

The contributions were more than welcome. With the hospital's dedication and opening but three months away, the hospital fund was still $20,000 short and the Board of Trustees was urging Methodists to give generously again so the hospital could open "without serious embarrassment." An appeal also went forward to help furnish the rooms in the hospital with sheets, pillowcases, towels, blankets, spreads and napkins. In a day when many of these items were made at home, donors were reminded that "a good quality is always the best." As a further help, volunteer seamstresses were provided with a list of various linen sizes.

The Board also chose its first hospital superintendent on New Year's Day in 1908. She was 34-year old Miss Marilla Williams, a deaconess of the Methodist Church since her consecration at Bedford, Indiana in 1901 and for the past eight years the superintendent of the Deaconess Hospital of Jeffersonville, Indiana. One of two women to

Methodist Hospital's first superintendent was Miss Marilla Williams, 34 years old, a deaconess of the Methodist Episcopal Church and former superintendent of the Deaconess Hospital, Jeffersonville, Ind. One of two women to apply for the post, she was selected from 60 applicants. All male candidates were physicians.

apply for the post, Miss Williams was selected from 60 applicants of which nine had been nominated for the position. The other nominees were males and physicians.

The January issue of *The Good Samaritan* described the new superintendent as "tall and distinguished looking" and reported, "she is said to possess executive ability to a marked degree." Her photograph on the front page of the magazine shows a sensitive and thoughtful woman with sad eyes and an unsmiling mouth set in a long, oval face with chestnut hair combed softly back. In all, she gives the impression of a serious, competent, no nonsense young lady.

With the appointment of Miss Williams, recruiting of other key staff members was launched. One of the primary needs was to put together a competent nursing staff. A Miss Goldsmith R.N., Deaconess, was appointed superintendent of nurses and director of the hospital's training school for nurses, which was to be an integral part of the hospital. Miss Goldsmith, however, served but for a few months and was replaced by Miss Margaret Lehman, R.N., a graduate of the Philadelphia General Hospital School of Nursing. Miss Lehman is generally regarded as the first superintendent of nurses by virtue of her contributions to the hospital organization.

A nurses' training school had been part of the hospital plan since its inception and with the planned opening of the hospital, recruitment of students began in earnest. Beginning as well as advanced students were accepted including transfers from other schools. Among the transfers were students who came to Methodist as the result of the merger of the State Medical College Hospital with the Indiana University Medical College. Three students transferred from St. Vincent Hospital, Indianapolis, and one from Presbyterian Hospital, Chicago. Methodist ministers and members of their churches throughout the state assisted in directing young ladies of "good character and background" to the Methodist school.

Other key appointments included that of Miss Jessie Bass, R.N., a graduate of the Protestant Deaconess Hospital School of Nursing, Indianapolis, who was placed in charge of the operating room in the basement. Miss Bass reported for duty some six weeks before the hospital opening to assist in the critical work of preparing the operating room for its first patients.

THE FIRST GRADUATING CLASS

CLASS OF 1911

The fourteen young ladies shown above are members of the 1911 graduating class of the Methodist Hospital School of Nursing and the first class to attend all three years of the school. Opened in 1908, the school graduated two students in 1909, five in 1910. By 1919, a total of 206 students were in training.

On the recommendation of the Administrative Committee for Interns, Drs. Harry Bond and Clifford Hirshfield were unanimously approved by the Board of Trustees to become Methodist Hospital's first interns. Compensation was fixed at $50 a year and it was ordered that the doctors be furnished with three white duck suits, their cost not to exceed $4.00.

On November 13, 1908, corresponding secretary D.M. Wood was appointed to the office of Chaplain with full authority to arrange for religious needs and services at the hospital.

Some salaries of the day are worth noting. Nurses received up to $40 a month and the superintendent of nurses, $75 a month. Interns and nurses were on 20 hour duty. Night engineers, who ran the boilers and the heating system, were paid $60 a month for 12 hour shifts. Miss Williams as superintendent received $80 a month and her lodging and board.

A schedule of hospital fees was drawn up and approved. Patient charges ranged from $7 a week for a bed in the medical ward to $25 and $30 for special rooms on the first, second, or third floors. The daily rate for fractional weeks ranged from $1 to $4.50 and it was established, as ongoing hospital policy, that no fees were to be for less than one week and all bills were to be payable in advance. (These low rates, of course, are in sharp contrast to today's hospital costs, but it is well to bear in mind that in 1908 a loaf of bread cost five cents and a dollar a day was considered a fair wage.)

Among other policy decisions was one dealing with indigent patients. "The poor who are unable to pay," the Board decided, "will be cared for free of charge to the extent of our ability" and all records of those cared for without charge will be "confidential." The Indianapolis District Epworth League provided additional help for the poor. The League paid for the building and equipping of Hospital Room 105 as a "free room" and raised $400 to maintain it for the district year 1908-1909.

These actions were in the Methodist tradition. Since the Church's founding and the days of John Wesley, Methodists had been concerned with the poor and the sick, the uneducated and the "spiritually lost."

Wesley had been more than a minister. He had also practiced preventive and curative medicine and earned the right to be called a physician. He studied medicine in his spare time after being appalled at the low estate of medicine in 18th Century England and the growing need to provide medical help to the poor. He opened dispensaries in London, Newcastle and Bristol; in his extensive travels he was always ready to give medical advice to those who needed it. His well known and widely read *Primitive Physick or the Easy and Natural Way to Cure Most Diseases*, published in 1747, went through 32 editions. Today it is still a valuable source for an assessment of 18th century medical practice and knowledge.

Wesley also anticipated many 20th century medical concepts. Years before the discovery of the germ theory, Wesley sensed the relationship between disease and poor hygiene and, in the words of one writer, "became the greatest force for hygiene and preventive medicine in his day." The saying, "Cleanliness is next to Godliness" is from one of Wesley's sermons.

Wesley was also among the first to consider the

John Wesley, founder of Methodism, opening a medical dispensary at Bristol, England, in 1746. Shocked by the low state of medicine in England, Wesley studied medicine, qualified as a physician, wrote a book, Primitive Physik which outlined cures for most diseases, and opened dispensaries in London and Newcastle as well as Bristol. Although the germ theory would not be discovered for another century, Wesley preached good hygiene as a means to good health. The saying, "Cleanliness is next to Godliness" is from one of Wesley's sermons. (Photo of an original oil painting at the Chicago Wesley Memorial Hospital.)

connection between pain and emotional distress and the need to treat the "whole man." He had visited a woman with a continual pain in her stomach who had been treated by doctors who had prescribed drug upon drug, "without knowing a jot of the matter concerning the root of the disorder." And whence came this woman's pain, Wesley asked? From fretting for the death of her son. "Why," Wesley asked, "then do not all physicians consider how bodily disorders are caused or

(viii)

that old unfashionable medicine, prayer. And have faith in God who " *killeth and* " *maketh alive, who bringeth down to the* " *grave, and bringeth up.*"

7. For the fake of thofe who defire, through the blefling of God, to retain the health which they have recovered, I have added a few plain, eafy rules, chiefly tranfcribed from Dr. Cheyne.

I. 1. The air we breath is of great confequence to our health. Thofe who have been long abroad in eafterly or northerly winds, fhould drink fome thin and warm liquor going to bed, or a draught of toaft and water.

2. Tender people fhould have thofe who lie with them, or are much about them, found, fweet, and healthy.

3. Every one that would preferve health, fhould be as clean and fweet as poffible in their houfes, clothes, and furniture.

II. 1. The great rule of eating and drinking, is, To fuit the quality and quantity of the food to the ftrength of our digeftion; to take always fuch a fort and fuch a meafure of food, as fits light and eafy on the ftomach.   2. All

(ix)

2. All pickled, or fmoaked, or falted food, and all high-feafoned, is unwholefome.

3. Nothing conduces more to health, than abftinence and plain food, with due labour.

4. For ftudious perfons, about eight ounces of animal food, and twelve of vegetable, in twenty four hours is fufficient.

5. Water is the wholefomeft of all drinks; quickens the appetite, and ftrengthens the digeftion moft.

6. Strong, and more efpecially fpirituous liquors, are a certain, though flow, poifon.

7. Experience fhews, there is very feldom any danger in leaving them off all at once.

8. Strong liquors do not prevent the mifchiefs of a furfeit, nor carry it off fo fafely as water.

9. Malt liquors (except clear fmall beer, or fmall ale, of a due age) are exceeding hurtful to tender perfons.
                                    10. Coffee

Pages from the 22nd edition of John Wesley's *Primitive Physik: An Easy and Natural Method of Curing Most Diseases,* which was originally published in 1747. It remains a valuable source for assessing 18th century medical practice and knowledge.

influenced by the mind, and in those cases which are utterly out of their sphere call in the assistance of the minister?"

Wesley's rules for good health as set forth in his *Primitive Physick* are for every age including our own. With brevity, clearness and a quaintness of language, he deals with cleaness, diet, sleep, exercise, regularity of natural habits and the influence of the passions upon health. He recommends, for instance: "Use as much exercise daily in the open air as you can without weariness. Sup at six or seven on the lightest food. Go to bed early and arise betimes."

Wesley left his stamp upon his Church. Methodism brought a sense of purpose and worth of life to its members. A selfless Christian became the Methodist ideal, an ideal reflected in concern for the sick and the poor and in its churches, universities and hospitals.

The new Methodist Hospital in Indianapolis would carry on the meanings and purpose of John Wesley's Church - "do all the good you can."

Chapter Three

A 'Blessed Ministry' Begins

"I was hungered, and ye gave me meat; I was thirsty, and ye gave me drink; I was a stranger and ye took me in; naked, and ye clothed me; I was sick, and ye visited me; I was in prison and ye came unto me . . . Inasmuch as ye have done it unto one of the least of these, my brethren, ye have done it unto me."
—Jesus
Mt 25: 35-38, 40   KJV

Methodist Hospital, 1908. The three story 65-bed unit was formally dedicated and opened with a four-day celebration that began on April 25.

Dedication of the new Methodist Hospital consisted of a four-day celebration that began on Sunday, April 26, 1908, with church services throughout the state and ended on the morning of the 29th with a formal dedication service at the hospital.

A spirit of thanksgiving characterized the Sunday services. As *The Good Samaritan* explained, the statewide services gave every Methodist an opportunity to participate in the hospital dedication as well as an additional opportunity to make a voluntary "thank you offering" over "the completion of this great and beneficent institution, which during the week will begin its blessed ministry to the sick and the suffering. . ."

Sunday in Indianapolis was marked by an additional event, an Epworth League rally at the Roberts Park Methodist Church, where many would recall the beginnings of an idea whose time had now come. Dr. Halstead, who had labored so long and faithfully as the first general secretary of the hospital, was the principal speaker. The Reverend Chasteen Smith, of Anderson, president of the State Epworth League, presided.

Roberts Park Methodist Church was also the scene of a mass meeting on Monday night with the Reverend Dr. W.A. Quayle of Chicago as the principal speaker. He was introduced by Indiana Governor J. Frank Hanley, who presided.

On Tuesday night 300 guests, including prominent church and lay persons, attended a glittering banquet at the hospital. A newspaper reporter commented "that every window (of the hospital) from its third floor to the basement was lighted in honor of the occasion and the assemblage was no less brilliant than the building itself." Toastmaster for the evening was former Governor Winfield T.

First floor surgery, Methodist Hospital, 1915.

Durban and the ladies of the Central Avenue Methodist Church served the banquet. The speakers were the Reverend H.A. Gobin, who would later become known as the "Grand Old Man of DePauw University"; Dr. John M. Kitchen, one of Indianapolis' oldest and most respected physicians; and the Reverend Dr. George Elliott of Chicago. The Reverend Joshua Stansfield pronounced the benediction.

Speakers recalled Methodism's long and proud history in helping the poor and sick, praised the philanthrophy of those who had made the hospital possible, and paid tribute to the Methodists of Indiana in establishing the hospital "as a monument to our faith." Dr. Gobin in his talk said that suffering aided people in rising above the differences in men—including ecclesiastical differences—and told the story of a Catholic sister who aided a

Methodist minister in obtaining bread and wine that he might administer the sacrament of the church to a dying Methodist in a Catholic hospital.

On Wednesday morning, April 29, 1908, the formal dedication exercises were held in the corridors of the second floor of the hospital highlighted by an address by the Reverend Dr. C.E. Bacon, president of the Board of Trustees, who, on that same day was being succeeded as president by W.C. Van Arsdel. The ritualistic services were read by the Reverend William D. Parr, a member of the Board of Trustees, the Reverend Joseph L. Stout and the Reverend A.H. DeLong, field secretaries. As part of the exercises, Miss Marilla Williams was formally installed as superintendent.

The newly opened hospital had 65 beds and included 37 private rooms, four large wards and three smaller wards. Representing a total outlay of $225,000, the three-story fireproof structure also included a heating and cooling plant with boilers possessing 600 horse power capacity, a system of scientific ventilation, two kitchens and "other accoutrements requisite to the carrying on of a modern hospital." Methodist was the 36th hospital to open its doors in Indiana and the ninth to be sponsored by a Protestant denomination. Of the other hospitals around the state, 13 were Roman Catholic institutions and 14 were supported by municipal appropriations or a local charity.

Further construction details of the new hospital were contained in an article in *The Good Samaritan*. Reporting on the new operating rooms, which it described as "comparing favorably with the best in the West," it said: "The floors are of white glass laid in large sheets so as to reduce the number of joints to minimum. The walls to a height of six feet are wainscoted with the same white glass." The operating room was also heated and cooled independently by a combination of direct radiation and an electric fan system.

The hospital elevator was singled out for special praise. It was of the new "plunger type" and chosen for "the elements of safety the system offers." The car, according to the writer, "rests on a steel piston which raises it by means of water pressure. On the downward trip the piston descends into a well sunk in the ground, the same depth that the car rises. The car is large enough so that a litter with patient, accompanied by a nurse and physicians, can be accommodated."

The article went on to describe in glowing terms the hospital's portable bathtubs, plumbing equipped

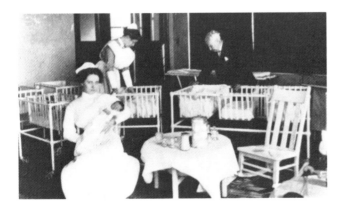

This handwritten report of 1909, listing doctors and the number of cases cared for, is a virtual "who's who" of early Indianapolis medicine. Dr. Goethe Link, in the left hand column with 21 cases, performed the first Caesarean operation at Methodist Hospital the following year. It was also among the first in Indiana.

with pedal action, dumbwaiters operated by push buttons, a call system of signal lights which "eliminated the continuous noise of clanging bells," and doors without panels or moldings with surfaces "as smooth as the top of a highly polished dining room table." Even the smoke stack of radial bricks came in for favorable comment: it was an uncommon five feet wide and 125 feet high.

With Miss Williams firmly at the helm, the new Methodist Hospital quickly settled into the daily and often dramatic routine of a major hospital. The first operations were performed. The school of nursing opened. Victims of railroad, horse and wagon and trolley accidents were treated. The first indigent patients were admitted to Room 105. On May 21, 1908 the hospital welcomed its first baby, a boy named Fletcher, born to the Reverend and Mrs. David O. Ernsberger, missionaries to India and home on furlough. (Fletcher, unhappily,

An unidentified doctor is making his rounds of the Methodist Hospital Nursery in this photograph taken about 1915. The first baby born at Methodist, Fletcher Ernsberger, was delivered on May 21, 1908 by Dr. Oliver G. Neier. The baby's parents, the Rev. and Mrs. David O. Ernsberger, were missionaries to India, home on furlough. (Methodist Hospital Archives.)

Resident Doctors 1914-15
Top Row—Left to Right: Dr. Oilar, Dr. Donaldson, Dr. Mueller, Dr. Bitler, Dr. Smith. Bottom Row—Dr. Moulder, Dr. Johnston.

would be killed in a hunting accident when he was 16 years of age.)

From the beginning the hospital operated from near capacity to capacity. A report of the first two months of operation showed that more than 100 patients had been treated. Patients came from all over the state and represented all creeds as well as those "who subscribed to no creed." The hospital was also running in the red. The treasurer's report for November of 1908 showed income of $2,994.28 with expenses of $4,726.66 leaving a deficit of $1,732.38. By December the deficit had risen to $2,100.

Those early months of the hospital's operation were busy ones for the Board of Trustees. One of the urgent policy decisions was that of admitting blacks in a day when segregation was a fact of life. For the Board and especially its members who were ministers, the admission of blacks posed a moral as well as a social dilemma for a hospital presumably "open to all." The Board voted on August 10, 1908 that a section of the hospital be set aside exclusively for black patients. The Board decision was perhaps not entirely in the Wesleyan tradition, but it was a small victory over prejudice at a time when many blacks were refused admission to private hospitals.

Among other decisions there was coal to be ordered, carloads of it, for the coming winter; a temporary loan to be negotiated to pay off the contractors; requests for salary increases to be considered; gifts to be acknowledged and plans developed for a children's ward as well as the possibility of expanding the present facilities to accommodate more patients. There were also some adjustments made to the hospital rate schedule: patients who furnished their own nurses would be charged $5 a week instead of $7 and Methodist clergymen and their families were to receive one-third off regular rates. And, because it was obvious the hospital was not large enough, partitions were set up to provide more beds for patients and a

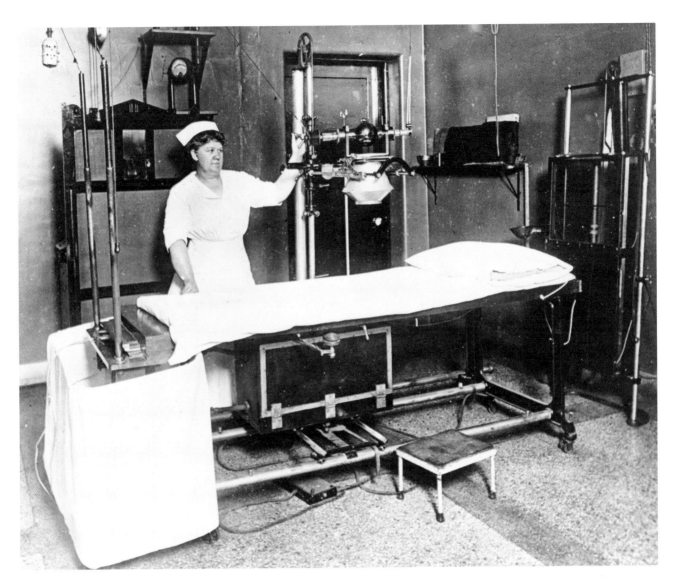

A lady of "firsts" at Methodist Hospital. Miss Jessie Bass, R.N., was the first operating room supervisor when the hospital opened in 1908 and, later, as shown in this 1924 photo, the first woman X-ray technician. Miss Bass also designed the distinctive nurses' cap of the School of Nursing. (Photo, courtesy Radiology Department.)

committee appointed to look into using the nurses' home as an annex for patients at rates lower than regular hospital rates. The committee was also to report on the possiblity of renting a house in the immediate neighborhood to be used as a residence for the displaced nurses.

The year 1909 brought many changes and new decisions. Early in the year, Miss Williams tendered her resignation as hospital superintendent, which the board promptly accepted. The possibility that there may have been some friction between Miss Williams and the Board may perhaps explain the Board's male chauvinistic action of March 5,

1909: by unanimous vote it was decided "the next superintendent would be a man." Another woman, however, served briefly as acting superintendent. Miss Margaret Lehman, superintendent of nurses, ran the hospital from March to July 1909, before resigning to become superintendent of visiting nurses in Philadelphia. She was succeeded as acting superintendent by Dr. J. McLean Moulder of Kokomo.

The new superintendent, appointed by the Board of Trustees later in the year, was W.T. Graham, M.D., of Brooklyn, New York, who had served for eleven years as resident manager of that city's Methodist hospital. Commenting on his appointment, a Methodist publication said: "We do not hesitate to say that he is a tested and tried hospital manager."

The year 1909 also marked the beginning of to-

Methodist Hospital Administrative officers, 1914-15. Top row (Left to Right) Ruby Roberts, Pharmacist; Mary Fergusson, Supervisor of Obstetrics; Harriett Rottler, Matron; Florence Rottler, Clerk; Margaret Dimmitt, Dietitian. Bottom row (Left to Right) Bertha Seward, Asst. Supervisor of Nurses; Jessie F. Bass, Supervisor of Surgery; Dr. J. McLean Moulder, Superintendent of Hospital; Rebecca G. Galt, Supervisor of Nurses; Edna Fletcher, Night Supervisor.

day's modern radiology department. Dr. Albert M. Cole founded the first X-ray department in an unused hospital room, eight by ten feet, in which he installed one of the earliest X-ray machines. Invented in 1895 by Wilhelm Roentgen of the University of Wurzburg and developed further by Thomas A. Edison, the machine's name was derived from the fact that the phenomenon of photographing the inside of the human body was an unknown quantity or X, hence the term X-ray. Methodist Hospital's first X-ray machine was a primitive affair by today's standards, using a Crookes gas tube and heavy glass plates. The process was cumbersome and uncertain. Since the hospital had no facilities for developing the plates, they had to be taken downtown, usually by a messenger on the electric street car, to Dr. Cole's office for processing. More often than not, the plates were unexposed because the tube was defective. This meant that Dr. Cole had to return to the hospital and start the process all over again.

In 1909 the need for additional hospital beds became critical and the Board of Trustees made preliminary plans for adding a new pavilion. By 1910 the shortage worsened and Dr. Graham, the hospital superintendent, reported to the Board in April that the hospital was refusing patients each month because of a lack of beds.

Dr. W. T. Graham, M.D. served as superintendent of Methodist Hospital from 1909 to 1911. Formerly of Brooklyn, N.Y., he had served eleven years as resident manager of that city's Methodist Hospital. He succeeded acting superintendent Dr. J. McLean Moulder.

Many referral patients from nearby towns often came to Methodist Hospital by way of the several interurban lines that terminated in the world's largest Traction Terminal on West Market Street, open since 1904. The site is now occupied by the Blue Cross-Blue Shield of Indiana Building.

A key factor in the need to expand was the rapid growth of the city of Indianapolis and central Indiana. Since 1900 the city's population had increased by nearly 65,000 and was still growing (in fact, would show an increase of 145,030 by 1920.) Indianapolis was a major manufacturing center and its excellent transportation facilities, which included railroads and interurbans, were attracting still more industries. The city had been among the first to manufacture and assemble the new automobiles and in 1907 ranked fourth among U.S. automakers. (The automobile was also beginning to account for accident victims who required hospitalization. In 1906 the State Board of Health reported three traffic fatalities; in 1915 it recorded 100 auto-related deaths.)

Methodism itself was also a very real factor in the need to expand. The largest denomination in the city, state and nation, Methodists preferred to go to their own hospital when accident or illness struck. A 1906 survey showed there were six million Methodists in the nation of which 210,593 were in Indiana (21.7% of the state's religious groups). No precise figures are available for Indianapolis, but with more than 40 Methodist churches located in various parts of the city, its membership was not only large but dominant. Indiana Methodists could also feel, by virtue of their contributions, that Methodist Hospital was *their* hospital. They were part of "a blessed ministry."

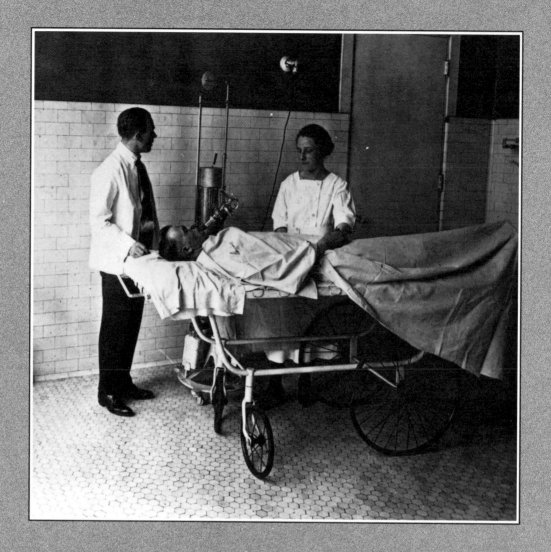

Chapter Four

Years of Growth and Change

> "The great vocation of
> the minister (Church) is
> to continuously make
> connections between the
> human story and the
> divine story."
> —*The Living Reminder*
> Henri J. M. Nouwen

As it became increasingly apparent that Methodist Hospital must expand its facilities in order to carry out its commitment to Church and community, the Board of Trustees in 1910 voted to construct two additional pavilions at a cost of $250,000.

Originally the Board had authorized the construction of a single new pavilion at a cost of $130,000, which was to include the current floating deficit of $15,600. Board President Charles W. Fairbanks suggested, however, that in the light of demands being made on the hospital, it would be more logical to build two new units and the Board concurred. It was also decided that provision be made for a children's ward on the third floor of the second pavilion. Funds for the ward were to be contributed by children of Methodist Sunday Schools.

The Board moved speedily to make the new buildings a reality. Architect Arthur Bohn—now going it alone since the death of his partner, Bernard Vonnegut in 1908—was called in to draw plans and these were quickly approved. Just as promptly the board called for bids and contractors were told that the work was to be finished "at the earliest possible moment."

To finance the new pavilions, a state-wide fund raising campaign was set up which included a canvass for $1,000 subscriptions, the donors to be entitled to "two plates" at a banquet which would mark the close of the drive. President Fairbanks, who had earlier contributed $5,000 to the hospital, and several other members of the Board set an example by being the first to pledge $1,000.

Other funds were being made available to the hospital by way of gifts, memorials, annuities and endowments from individuals and organizations.

Methodist Hospital's Emergency Room was one of the best equipped in Indiana when this photograph was taken a few years after the hospital's opening.

In earlier days when the original hospital was being built there had been only a few of these—the earliest being a bequest from Mrs. Jamima Darby of Kokomo and a memorial endowment of more than $8,000 from Martha Ray as well as gifts and endowments from the Epworth League, the Women's Guild and the Women's Home Missionary Society of the Methodist Episcopal Church. Additional financial support came from Indianapolis physicians who gave generously to the new hospital.

By 1917 funds from these sources were coming in at a fairly regular rate, the amounts ranging from $100 to $100,000, the latter sum representing the sale of a 240-acre farm as part of the Messick estate. Other parcels of land given or willed to the hospital included 200 acres of "improved land" with a value of $40,000, the gift of Mrs. Adams of Frankfort. In fact, it was a substantial bequest in the will of Mrs. Mary S. Yount that made possible

the construction of the first pavilion, which was named in her honor. During her lifetime, Mrs. Yount had been a devout member of the First Methodist Episcopal Church of Shelbyville and one of the earliest supporters of the hospital.

The cornerstone of the Mary S. Yount Pavilion was laid on July 25, 1911 and about 300 persons attended the ceremony to hear the principal address by Bishop David H. Moore of Cincinnati, Ohio. President Fairbanks presided.

Opened in 1913, the new pavilion increased the hospital's capacity to 155 beds, but still the hospital could not care for all those applying for admission. Nor did it catch up with demand when the second unit, the North Pavilion, cost $133,000, was opened in 1916 to increase the number of hospital beds to 250 and make it the largest hospital in the city as well as the state. Meanwhile two additional hospitals had opened in Indianapolis, both in 1914: the Robert W. Long and St.

Methodist Hospital, 1915. Although the hospital was only seven years old, it had already added a new pavilion on either side of the original structure to take care of the growing demand for patient services.

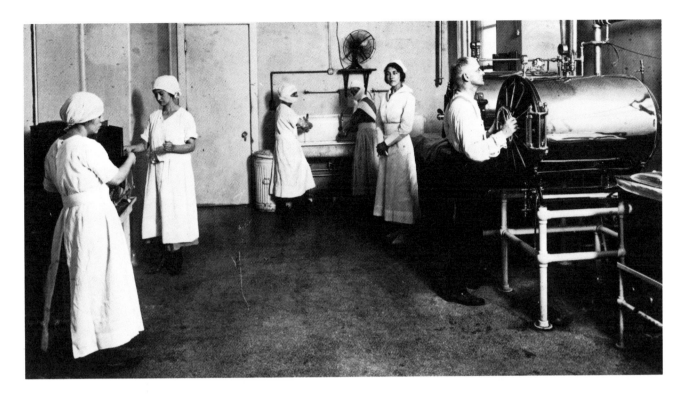

In sharp contrast to today's state-of-the art equipment, Central Service worked, before 1920, with limited equipment to sterilize supplies for surgery. Note the primitive unit at far right.

Francis Hospitals. Despite these additions to the health care delivery system and the expansion of Methodist Hospital, a shortage of beds continued to plague hospital administrators.

Although Methodist Hospital posted regular deficits ($3,776, for example, in November 1914) there was no attempt to raise the generally low hospital rates. This was in keeping with a policy established by the Indiana Conference and the Board of Trustees back in 1902 "to keep (rates) close to the needs of the people" and "that ample provision be made to care for the sick and injured from families of unskilled working men, who live by a low day wage, so that they may have access to attractive private rooms at prices within their reach, which will allow them to be independent." Hospital costs, however, continued to rise, especially during World War I, and in a comment, reminiscent of our own times, the hospital superintendent in 1917 called the Board's attention to the fact that "eggs, butter, milk and meat cost us enormously last month."

Increasing demands on the hospital for the care of the poor, posed some financial problems but the hospital was firm in its decision that no one was to be turned away because of inability to pay. In the first year of the hospital's operation, one in six patients had been a charity case, a situation which continued to increase. From an estimated cost of $3,000 in its first year, the hospital was spending $25,000 in 1911 for patients unable to pay. To offset the rising costs and confirm its commitment to the poor, the Indiana Conference in 1910 approved an annual apportionment of ten cents from each member of the state's Methodist Churches to go into a "Sustentation Fund" to enable the hospital to continue and, in fact, increase its charitable work. Additional assistance came in the form of gifts or endowments accompanied by the stipulation that the money or the interest on the money be used to provide for those unable to pay. *The Methodist Episcopal Discipline* of 1912 declared, "Our hospitals should be ready always to receive the sick poor recommended by pastors under proper rules and regulations, not as charity patients, but as guests of the Church...Our church hospitals... should employ a pastor, deaconess or other Christian worker, to give special attention to those in need of spiritual help.."

The Board took a positive step to assure quality medical leadership and service for the patients on May 26, 1909 when the bylaws were amended to provide for a Medical Advisory Board. Doctors appointed to this board were: Henry Jameson,

A.C. Kimberlin, F.B. Wynn, R.O. Alexander, O.G. Pfaff, John H. Oliver, William N. Wishard, Thomas Noble, E.D. Clark, C.B. McCullough, J.F. Barnhill, Theodore Potter, H.O. Pantzer, A.B. Graham and N.D. Woodward.

The year 1912 brought another change in superintendents. Dr. Graham who had served since 1909, resigned to accept the superintendency of the Methodist Hospital in Des Moines, Iowa, and was succeeded by Dr. J. McLean Moulder of Kokomo. Dr. Moulder served until 1915 when he was succeeded by Dr. Charles S. Woods. Each of the three men presided over a growing and expanding hospital at a critical period in the hospital's history. Although statistics are missing for many of those early years, it is known that in 1913 the hospital treated 2,690 patients for a total of more than 10,000 since the opening in 1908.

In other administrative moves the corporate name was shortened on April 20, 1915 to the Methodist Episcopal Hospital of Indiana. Other changes included the installation of an electric elevator with a speed of 200 feet per minute and telephones in all rooms and wards of the hospital. A house for nurses on Senate Avenue was converted to an isolation house for children with contagious diseases, and a building committee was named "to look into the enlargement of the hospital." In 1918 the hospital installed a new X-ray machine and assigned a technician for full time duty. "No other hospital," the trustees boasted, "has X-ray equipment to compare with ours."

Additional hospital space was acquired in 1917 by elevating the roof of the Central Building, cost $50,000, and moving the surgeries to the newly created floor. Coincident with the opening of the new floor, the Board voted to build a West Wing on the hospital "on a site north of the present building." Because of the continued and urgent need for more beds, the contractors were again urged to proceed with all possible speed.

The following year, 1918, the Board recognized the growing need for a nurses' home and purchased a site at 18th Street and Capitol Avenue for $11,000, paying $1,500 down and the balance in two annual installments of $4,750. The Methodist Hospital Guilds and the Home Missionary Societies around the state were assigned the task of raising the necesary funds. The home was badly needed as the student nurses were housed in cot-

A former mayor of Kokomo, Indiana, Dr. J. McLean Moulder, M.D., served as superintendent of Methodist Hospital from 1912 to 1914. Earlier, for a brief period in 1909, he had served as acting superintendent. He resigned to become superintendent of Bethany Methodist Hospital (now Bethany Medical Center) Kansas City, Kansas.

tages scattered around the hospital area including Capitol and Senate Avenues, Meridian Street and Hall Place. Ground for the new home was broken in 1919, but, unhappily, the building would not be completed for another nine years.

Methodist Hospital was justly proud of its School of Nursing, which had been a significant part of the hospital since its opening in 1908 and would continue to be throughout its history. Its first graduating class in 1909 consisted of two young women, the Misses Roxy Parker and Josephine Wilkinson. A second class of five students graduated the following year. A class of 14 graduated in 1911 and had the distinction of being the first class to attend all three years of the hospital's school. By 1919 a total of 206 students were in training and the hospital estimated the annual cost of operating the school at $25,000.

Dr. Charles S. Woods, Superintendent of Methodist Hospital, from 1915 to 1922, is seen here dictating to his secretary, Ada Frost. A graduate of Rush Medical College, Chicago, Dr. Woods was also a professional administrator and when he left Methodist held com-

parable supervisory positions with St. Luke's Hospital, Cleveland, and Methodist Central Hospital, Peoria, Ill. During Dr. Woods' tenure, the first organization of physicians, the Clinical Research Society, was completed. It was replaced later by the Medical Staff. (Photo Methodist Hospital Archives.)

Dietitian Margaret Dimmit (at left) supervises preparation of a meal about 1915. Methodist Hospital's light and airy kitchens with screened

windows, were located on every floor. Note the big, old fashioned ice box behind Miss Dimmit.

The 1915 Junior Class of the School of Nursing pose for their photograph with Deaconess Wilson—center front row.

The superintendent of nurses also served as superintendent of the school of nursing and, with other nursing supervisors, taught some classes. For some unknown reason, superintendents were regularly changed in the early days of the school; most of the women who held the post served but a year or two. Miss Lehman, for example, who served from 1908 to 1909 was succeeded by Miss Lena Salmon of Chicago, who stayed from 1909 to 1910. She was succeeded by Miss Julia Adams of Albany, New York, who held the post from 1910 to 1911. Miss Jessie Horn, a graduate of the School of Nursing, Chicago, stayed the longest, from 1911 to 1914. Miss Rebecca Galt of Philadelphia took over the reins from 1914 to 1916 and was succeeded by Miss Frances Marsh, also of Philadelphia, who held the post from 1916 to 1917.

The first graduate of the Methodist Hospital School of Nursing to serve as superintendent was Miss June Gray, class of 1915, who served from 1917 to 1918 and then resigned to serve as a nurse in World War I. Miss Gray was followed by two other Methodist graduates: Miss Edith Mitch, class of 1913, who served from 1918 to 1920 and Miss Fannie Paine, class of 1916, who filled the position from 1920 to 1924. Hospital records indicate that most of those who held the superintendency had

earlier served as supervisors or assistants to the superintendent.

Students were not required to pay tutition fees until 1932, and the early students of the School of Nursing received not only their room and board but a monthly pay check. Mrs. Katherine Brewer Pattison, a member of the class of 1911, says the monthly pay was $6 and if the student broke anything the cost of the breakage was deducted from her check.

In a day when every young lady was expected to know how to sew, students made their own uniforms. The earliest nurses' uniforms were of blue gingham with a floor length skirt and long sleeved blouse, starched white collar and cuffs six to eight inches long, a white bib and apron, black shoes and stockings. The student's white cap was designed by Jessie Bass, the operating room supervisor.

Until 1917 nurses worked in the hospital from 7 a.m. to 7 p.m. and following their twelve hour shift, attended evening classes in the hospital basement. In 1917, however, the day was shortened to eight hours of clinical experience plus classes. In addition to their regular nursing duties, nurses also dry mopped floors and dusted. Protocol demanded that whenever a doctor came into view, nurses were to immediately snap to respectful attention. "Discipline was strict," Mrs. Pattison said, "and we all walked the straight and narrow." There were also demerits and penalties for infractions of the rules, but Mrs. Pattison confesses she was never penalized because "I was too scared to break any rules."

The first published year book of the School of Nursing, dated 1915, shows that nursing supervisors generally taught such subjects as practical nursing, surgical nursing, and massage while hospital staff doctors gave courses in anatomy, bacteriology, obstetrics, gynecology and other medical subjects. Included in the school's faculty was Dr. Lillian Mueller of Indianapolis, the first

woman doctor to become a member of the Methodist Hospital staff. There may, however, have been a hint of male chauvinism in assigning her to teach, "bandaging."

Despite the strict discipline and equally strict rules of conduct, students and nurses found time for after hours fun although it meant clandestine meetings and breaking hospital school rules. Mrs. Pattison recalled that student nurses and interns were forbidden to "keep company," but they

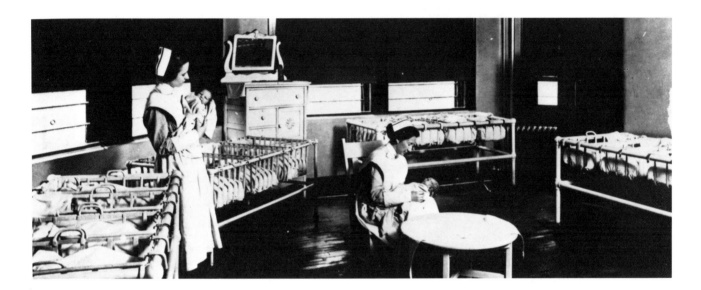

Methodist Hospital's Nursery (circa 1915-1918) lacked today's sophisticated equipment, but loving care was as much in evidence then as now.

Methodist Hospital nurses show off their white over blue uniforms in this photograph taken around 1913. The bodices were usually starched to give them a white, crisp look and pressed with a hand iron. Equally long skirts were also worn after hours in those long gone days. (Methodist Hospital Archives)

Course of Study

SENIORS.

Bacteriology	Dr. Alburger
Nose and Throat	Dr. Barnhill
Nervous Diseases	Dr. Neu
Children's Diseases	Dr. Mumford
Gynecology	Dr. Link
General Surgery	Dr. Eberwein

INTERMEDIATES.

Surgical Nursing	Miss Bass
Dietetics	Miss Dimmitt
Obstetrics	Dr. Jackson
Bandaging	Dr. Lillian Mueller
Infectious Diseases	Dr. Duckworth
Hygiene and Sanitation	Dr. Shimer
Urinalysis	Dr. Hamer
Massage	Miss Dunlop

JUNIORS.

Practical Nursing	Miss Galt, Miss Thatcher
Anatomy	Dr. Duckworth
Bacteriology	Dr. Johnston
Materia Medica	Dr. Rinker

The Methodist Hospital School of Nursing Course of Study.

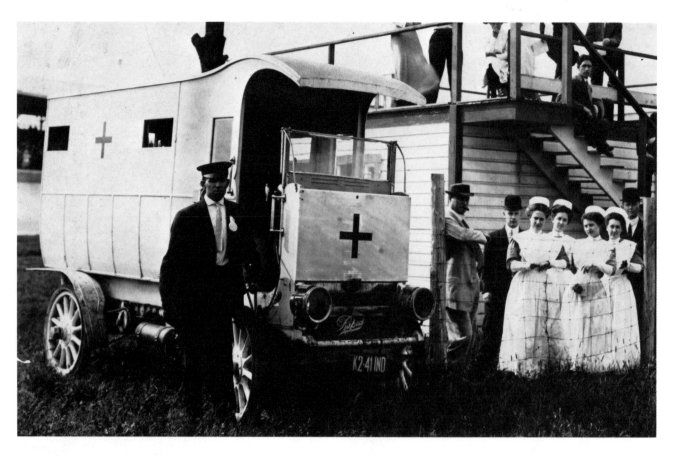

Methodist Hospital's long time continuing relationship with the Indianapolis Motor Speedway harks back to the track's earliest days, even before the first 500-mile race in 1911. Shown here in this 1910 photograph is the first motorized ambulance in Indianapolis (from the Flanner and Buchanan Mortuary) poised to speed patients to Methodist Hospital. Standing beside the ambulance is the driver, John "Pat" Patterson, Dr. H.R. Allen and student nurses: Kitty Brewer, Jeanette Taylor, Wilma Entsminger and Marjorie Hunt.
(Photo courtesy Mrs. John Tacoma, daughter of Mr. Patterson.)

managed to meet at the streetcar line on Illinois Street and ride downtown together for dances in the Maennerchor Building or attend stage plays and the popular silent movies at local theaters. If a nurse stayed out past the strictly enforced 10 p.m. curfew, there was always an obliging roommate or fellow conspirator to open a window for the wayward nurse.

Nurses and doctors were among the first to be recruited when America declared war on Germany on April 6, 1917. Drs. John Oliver and O.G. Pfaff of the Methodist Advisory Board joined with Drs. David Ross and Frank Morrison to form the 500-bed Eli Lilly Base Hospital, which later became the U.S. Army's Base Hospital 32 and were stationed at Contrexeville in the Vosges Mountains about 350 miles from Paris. Miss June Gray resigned as superintendent of nurses to join the Base Hospital, bringing with her a group of Methodist Hospital nurses.

Meanwhile on the home front, Indianapolis helped put four Liberty Loans over the top and observed wheatless Mondays, meatless Tuesdays, heatless days, lightless days and Sundays without gasoline. Families planted Victory Gardens. The city's industries mobilized to turn out weapons of war. Prest-O-Lite made munitions. Allison's revised and rebuilt Liberty airplane engines while the Indianapolis Motor Speedway became an aviation repair depot. Best selling sheet music in downtown stores included "Over There," "K-K-K-Katy," "Oh! How I Hate to Get Up in the Morning," "The Rose of No Man's Land," "Hinky-Dinky Parlez Vous," and "Just a Baby's Prayer at Twilight for Her Daddy Over There."

The years 1918-1919 brought an epidemic of influenza that killed twenty million people worldwide including 548,000 in the United States. No respecter of persons, influenza attacked all ages and all classes including the doctors and nurses who sought to bring the epidemic under control. In Indianapolis, it invaded the Vocational Home for Soldiers, the State Institution for the Blind, and the state's largest army training center, Fort Benjamin Harrison. In response to a request from the Fort's commanding officer, all of the city's hospitals dispatched scores of nurses to help care for the sick and dying soldiers. Methodist Hospital responded generously and sent a supervisor and thirteen student nurses, nearly all of whom eventually contracted the influenza virus. In 1919 the epidemic invaded the Methodist Hospital School of Nursing and took the lives of two young student nurses. Among other hospital deaths was that of a Miss Fletcher, the night supervisor.

On November 11, 1918, while the influenza epidemic still raged, Indianapolis cheered itself hoarse as word of the armistice ending the war reached the city. There was dancing in the corridors of Methodist Hospital as doctors, patients and nurses celebrated the Allied Victory. Downtown cheering, shouting, wild-with-joy masses of people packed the streets and paraded around the Circle. Church bells, fire bells, factory whistles, sirens, streetcar bells and automobile horns added to the din, even invading the quiet of churches where many had gone to offer prayers of thanksgiving.

In May of 1919, the city cheered itself hoarse again as the soldiers of the 150th Field Artillery and doctors, nurses and enlisted men of Base Hospital 32, back from the war, marched under a great victory arch spanning North Meridian Street. As they marched around the Circle, with bands playing and flags waving, a living red cross was formed on the steps of the Soldiers and Sailors Monument.

Although few knew it, the end of World War I also marked the end of an era and the beginning of another—an era that would bring revolutionary changes in medicine, surgery and hospital care.

Methodist Hospital, Princeton, Indiana

The success of Methodist Hospital, Indianapolis, and a growing need for additional hospital facilities around the state, spurred the construction of three other hospitals in Indiana between 1918 and 1924 for which Methodist Hospital assumed responsibility for management and operation.

The three new hospitals were: Princeton Methodist, opened in 1918, with 25 beds; Gary Methodist, opened in 1923, with 100 beds; and Fort Wayne Methodist, opened in 1923, with 150 beds. The Gary and Fort Wayne hospitals also incorporated nurses' training schools.

Indianapolis' Methodist Hospital supervised the operation of the three out-of-the city hospitals until the 1940s, when, at the request of the Board of Trustees, the three hospitals became autonomous.

Chapter Five

Plans and Philanthropists

"It is one of the most beautiful compensations of this life that no man can seriously help another without helping himself."
—Emerson

For six days in June of 1920 Indianapolis celebrated its one hundredth birthday with a series of events that included special musical programs, church services, speeches, three spectacular pageants, a downtown parade with 122 floats and a procession of decorated and illuminated barges on the White River. After the pomp and the pageantry were over, the swinging part of the population launched one of the giddiest, gaudiest, most tasteless, happiest and saddest eras in history.

The celebration inaugurated a decade that brought prohibition, speakeasies, hip flasks, roadhouses, the Ku Klux Klan, big bands, dance marathons, the flapper, the Florida land boom, bathing beauty contests, gangsters and a new brassy and blue sound called jazz.

Methodist Hospital's emergency room reflected the problems of the new decade. More and more men and women were being treated for alcohol poisoning as the result of drinking bootleg booze concocted in bath tubs, garages, backrooms, old warehouses or cellars. Marathon dancers were admitted for physical exhaustion brought on by dancing for days in the hope of a small cash prize. Quarrels over liquor and liquor shipments triggered arguments that frequently led to knifings and shootings or bootleggers being badly beaten up. Automobiles, however, took the heaviest toll in terms of accidents and fatalities. The introduction of easy payment plans and Henry Ford's Model T, known affectionately as "the flivver" and "the tin lizzie," placed an automobile within the reach of families of even modest means. The story is told that the Methodist Hospital parking lot was so filled with Fords, that an out of town visitor asked if there was a Ford dealer in the area.

The seven-story nurses' home, dedicated on November 8, 1928, was the gift of Mr. and Mrs. John W. Wile of Thorntown as a memorial to Mr. Wile's father, Jacob E. Wile, for whom the home was named. The new home provided rooms for 300 nurses on six floors with the seventh floor devoted to recreation and social purposes.

Hospitals were facing new shortages of beds and in 1925, it was estimated that Indianapolis was short 400 beds. Methodist Hospital reported that in only five weeks of the entire year of 1927 had they been able to accommodate all the patients seeking hospital care. And, on one particularly unhappy day, 27 surgical patients could not be registered because of lack of space. All of this occurred in a year when the hospital treated more than 12,000 patients including 8,882 surgical cases and reported 787 births.

The need for more hospital beds was confirmed in a survey conducted under the auspices of, and funded by, the Indianapolis Foundation. Its consultant, Dr. William H. Walsh, wrote that Methodist needed to expand "up to but not to exceed 600 beds." His summary report also recommended:

1. Departmentalization of the medical staff with the chiefs of each service serving on the Medical Advisory Board.
2. Examination of all tissue removed from patients by the clinical laboratory, whether or not the surgeon wants it done.
3. Reduction of laboratory costs so that every patient can have the benefit of the scientific advantage available in the hospital regardless of the patient's ability to pay.
4. Give "serious consideration to the establishment of an institution for convalescent patients, preferably removed from the smoke, dirt and noise of the city, to reduce costs to patients requiring mostly custodial care;"
5. Consider hiring a trained clinical record librarian to assume complete charge of records.

The continuing shortage of beds could not be ignored and in December of 1927, the Board of Trustees authorized plans for a 16-story (later reduced to eight stories) annex at a cost of more than a million dollars. The new structure would contain 400 rooms along with diet kitchens, preparation and treatment rooms and surgeries. Two entire floors were to be given over to the maternity department. And every room, according to plans of D. A. Bohlen and Son, would be sound proof and planned for outside exposure. The vote to build the new addition was taken at a time when the new nurses' home and a new laundry and power house were nearing completion.

The new seven-story nurses' home, which had

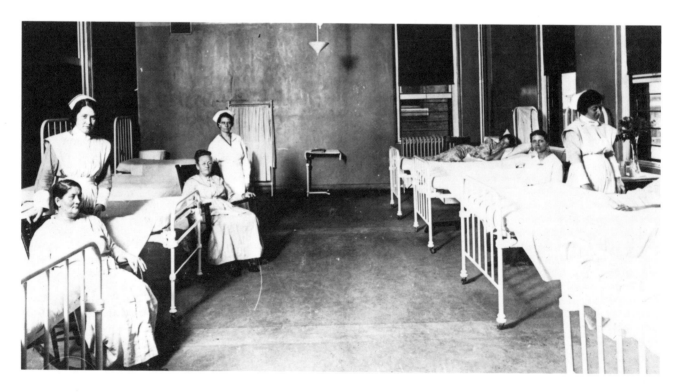

Women's ward, Methodist Hospital, about 1920.

REPORT FOR 1927

The number of patients admitted to the Indianapolis Methodist Hospital during 1927 was 12,224. This is a gain of 660 over 1926.

There were 8,882 surgical cases in 1927. 527 more than the previous year.

There was no accident in Anesthetics.

The number of births during the year was 787. A gain of 97.

1506 children were cared for during the year.

More than $101,000 in free service was given in 1927, or there was given during the year in free service $276.00 per day, or $11.50 per hour.

THE HOSPITAL

Hospitals have now reached a higher degree of development than ever before.

The value of their service to humanity depends largely upon the intelligence, skill and high ideals of the physicians on their Staff, the nurses in their employ and the girls in their Training School.

The Hospital represents an important business in any community, dealing not in the necessities of life but with life itself. It is not operated for financial gain, but seeks the higher reward, that of healing the sick.

The front (right) and back page of a condensed version of the 1927 annual report showing admissions of 12,224 for the year.

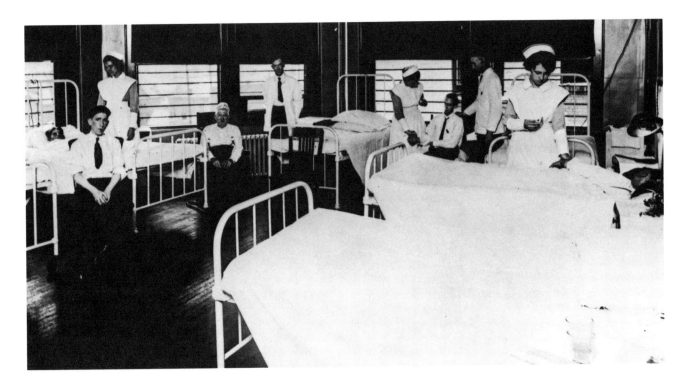

Men's ward, Methodist Hospital, 1920.

progressed slowly since its inception nine years before, was becoming a reality thanks to the gift of $200,000 from Mr. and Mrs. John W. Wile of Thorntown as a memorial to Mr. Wile's father, Jacob E. Wile, for whom the new home was to be named. The new home, north of the main hospital building on the northwest corner of Capitol Avenue and 18th Street, provided rooms for 300 nurses on the second to sixth floors. The seventh floor, consisting of a large open room with open porches on three sides, was devoted to social and recreational purposes. The first floor contained a lecture room, laboratories, equipment and supply rooms and a small dining and social hall. The south wing of the first floor incorporated a 300-seat auditorium which also served as a chapel.

More than 1,500 persons attended the dedication of Jacob E. Wile Hall on November 8, 1928. Opening day speakers included Bishop Edgar Blake of the Indianapolis area; the Reverend N.E. Davis of Chicago, executive secretary of the Board of Hospitals and Homes and Deaconess Work of the United Methodist Church; Mrs. Alma H. Scott, R.N., president of the Indiana State League of Nursing Education and executive secretary of the Indiana State Nurses' Association; and the Reverend George M. Smith. Reverend Smith had been superintendent of Methodist Hospital since his 1923 appointment to succeed the Reverend Dr. Demetrius Tillotson who had served for a year after Dr. Woods' resignation. Reverend Smith was the same man who back in 1899 had turned the tide in favor of the hospital project at the Indiana Conference.

The Reverend Davis praised the great work of the Methodist Church in caring for the sick and injured throughout the world and congratulated the Board of Trustees for its fine and benevolent work in Indiana. Arthur V. Brown, president of the Board, presided at the dedication and extended formal thanks to Mr. and Mrs. Wile for their splendid gift. The Reverend Smith called Mr. and Mrs. Wile, "the patron saints of student nurses" and described the new nurses' home as "an enduring memorial to a noble father by a devoted son." And he added, "This remarkable deed of philanthropy, which must have been inspired by the spirit and service of Christ, will write the names of John W. and Laura B. Wile high on the list of Indiana's public spirited, philanthropic citizens who are held in perpetual honor."

Methodist Hospital student nurses of an earlier day took each baby for a walk in the fresh air and sunshine at least twice daily, weather permitting. This 1918 photo shows Dorley Mae Nelson with one of her tiny charges. Those areas of white behind Miss Nelson are diapers, which were hand washed by student nurses and laid out on the grass to dry in the sun to "freshen them up." (Photo courtesy of Robert G. Whitinger, son of Dorley Mae Nelson Whitinger.)

In 1928, Methodist Hospital was classed among the ten largest hospitals in the United States, according to Arthur R. Baxter, vice president of the Board of Trustees, in a statement on the hospital's condition. With the completion of the new addition, he said Methodist would have a capacity of 600 beds which compared with Johns Hopkins' 784, the Henry Ford Hospital's 600 in Detroit and Presbyterian Hospital's 445 in Chicago. Indianapolis' Methodist Hospital was also rated in Class A by the American College of Physicians and Surgeons.

The X-Ray Department, supervised by Dr. Arthur C. Echternacht, was operating on a 24-hour day schedule and in 1928 treated 4,229 patients or 12

First chairman of the Clinical Research Society was Dr. Murray N. Hadley. The Society was founded in June of 1920 and was the progenitor of today's medical staff.

each day. X-ray was also being used for treatment as well as diagnosis and in the same year 565 persons received radium treatment.

Other departments in which the hospital could take special pride included anesthesiology. In a day when anesthetics and administering of anesthetics was still a comparatively new science, the hospital could boast of an eight-year record without a single accident. The department, under the direction of Dr. John M. Whitehead assisted by four specially trained physicians, administered anesthetics to more than 5,000 patients a year.

The 1920s also marked the organization of a Clinical Research Society with Dr. Murray N. Hadley as its first chairman. Progenitor of today's medical staff (they were not permitted then to use the word "staff" in their titles), the society was formed in June of 1920 with 57 physicians on the original roster, a number that swelled to 87 by the time the group held its first formal meeting on September 3. The purpose of the society, as spelled

out in the constitution and bylaws, was to increase the efficiency of the hospital and improve the professional standards of its members. In a very real sense, the society would function as a resident peer review group and provide continuing educational opportunities for its members. The hospital's interns were invited to participate without payment of dues. The Board of Trustees welcomed the formation of the society, viewing it as a positive step in assuring the maintenance of the high standards of the American College of Surgeons. At the September meeting, Dr. Homer C. Hamer was elected secretary and Drs. A.C. Kimberlin, John A. MacDonald, Ernest DeWofe Wales and Edgar F. Kiser were named to the executive committee.

Superintendent C.S. Woods was the speaker at the society's initial meeting and outlined the requirements of the American College of Surgeons (ACS) as it applied to standardization of hospitals, staff organizations, meetings and fee splitting. The members agreed to cooperate in every possible way to enable Methodist Hospital to continue to conform to ACS minimum requirements and agreed that "every member practicing fee splitting shall be expelled."

During the next four years the society dealt with a number of critical problems including a 1921 report that 80 case histories, important in the treatment of patients, had not been made by attending physicians. In the same year the first question of classification came up and each member was requested to classify himself "as to what he meant to do in the hospital." In July the society sharply reprimanded some of its members for supporting legislation which would compel all pay hospitals to be free and open to all duly licensed physicians of the state without membership in the society. Such legislation, the society officers made unmistakably clear, would be destructive to professional progress and prevent the hospital from protecting its patients against incompetent medical service. The society also policed itself. In 1924 the society authorized an offending physician to continue doing "simpler" operations but barred him from performing the more complex ones.

The society proved to be cooperative and helpful. When the College of Surgeons threatened to refuse accreditation unless records were more detailed and staff conferences devoted to analysis of end results, the society pledged its assistance. Accreditation continued on a Class A basis. The

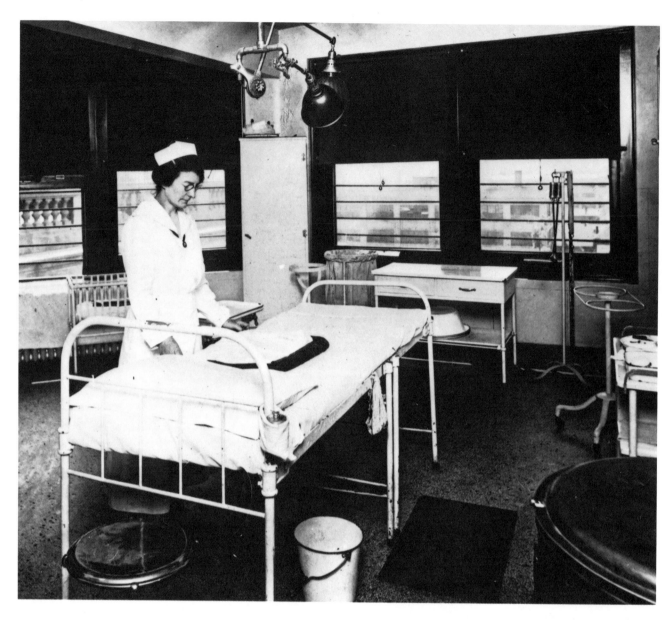

Methodist Hospital's Delivery Room, 1924. Miss Frances Macmillan, Superintendent of Nurses and the Nurses' Training School, seen here preparing for a prospective mother, remembers that the elevator frequently broke down and "we often carried the patients up the stairway from the fourth floor to the fifth floor delivery room."

society was also proud of its own. In 1922 it unveiled a memorial plaque in memory of Dr. Kimberlin and in 1923 a plaque for Dr. Frank B. Wynn, both early members of the Methodist Hospital staff and dedicated supporters of the hospital. Dr. Wynn, a member of the hospital advisory committee, was a well known physician, educator and naturalist. He was credited with being the principal catalyst in unifying various private schools into the Indiana University School of Medicine. The society sponsored the first formal

teaching of medicine at the hospital in May of 1922 when Dr. Raymond C. Beeler, offered a course in X-ray diagnosis. The Clinical Research Society continued its existence until January, 1925 when it was organized into a "Staff Society." Among the earliest acts of the new staff organization was the establishment of a library for interns and courses for the instruction of interns in X-ray and laboratory departments.

The laboratory of Methodist Hospital had assumed a key role in the hospital by the 1920s. In the beginning, it had been relegated to a small room, under the supervision of a consulting pathologist, Dr. Henry R. Alburger, and a part time laboratory worker. Its work, however, in the development of insulin and its continued value in medical therapeutics had made it one of the important departments of the growing hospital. Under Dr. Warvel, the department's first full-time director, and Dr. MacDonald, tremendous strides had been made and the laboratory grew and expanded. Doctors and hospital staff realized that laboratory examinations were a necessity in the admission of patients and an admission fee of one dollar was charged each new patient which covered the cost of a blood count, urine examination, smears, Phenolsulphonphthalein test or whatever other tests the doctor ordered. The dollar charge enabled the laboratory to become financially self sustaining.

Dr. Andrew J. Wallhauser served as laboratory chief from 1925-1927. During his tenure at the Methodist Hospital laboratory, attention and interest centered on experimental treatments of Hodgkin's Disease using extracts of diseased lymph nodes administered hypodermically. The work was carried out with the skilled help of Dr. John M. Whitehead. Considerable and sometimes spectacular success was reported by way of the new preparation. Following a brief tenure by Dr. George Garceau, Dr. Horace M. Banks was appointed laboratory chief in 1927. During his many years as laboratory chief, the department developed spectacularly.

Under the leadership of Dr. Banks, the new Chief of the Medical Research Laboratory, separate departments were established for Biochemistry, Bacteriology, Serology and Pathology, each headed by a trained and experienced technician. Despite limitations imposed by the Great Depression, the Medical Research Laboratory flourished and became increasingly important as Methodist Hospital physicians sought to raise the level of knowledge and competence in medical practice. Writing in 1927, Dr. Banks called the Methodist laboratory the "unseen factor" in the diagnosis and treatment of patients. For the doctor, he wrote, the laboratory "renders his procedures less obscure" and for the patient, the laboratory is a "semaphore through the traffic of therapy."

National acclaim came to Dr. Banks as the result of original research conducted in 1932-33 which produced a new and improved method for the administration of intravenous injections. Up to this time, such injections had been used carefully and sparingly because of the high incidence of reactions. Dr. Banks' work took on added importance during World War II when injections of plasma saved countless lives of wounded or ill soldiers. Today, intravenous injections are used routinely and unfavorable reactions are rare.

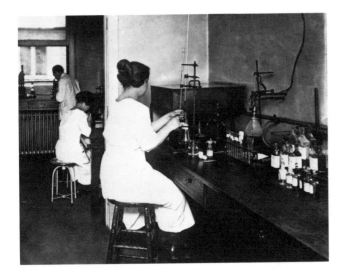

Laboratory facilities, Methodist Hospital, 1918. The laboratory in those long gone days consisted of two small rooms where two technicians and a part time consulting pathologist, Dr. Henry R. Alburger, conducted three or four blood tests and 15 urine examinations a day. This is in sharp contrast with the hospital's 1984 sophisticated clinical laboratories where an average of 5,479 tests are made daily.

Although a far cry from today's office with its computers, copiers and other modern office equipment, the filing department of Methodist Hospital was regarded as up-to-the-minute when this photograph was made in 1920.

Methodist Hospital, 1929. The steel framework, upper right, is for the new 200-bed general hospital financed by a gift from Mrs. Mary Hanson Carey in honor of her father, Julius A. Hanson. Behind the framework is Wile Hall, the new home for nurses.

With plans underway for a new hospital building, the Board of Trustees voted to raise the necessary million dollars to finance the new structure and appointed a prominent Indianapolis businessman, Arthur R. Baxter, vice president of the Board of Trustees, as campaign chairman. The new campaign was formally launched on May 12, 1929 on "Hospital Day," the birthday of Florence Nightingale, the famous "Angel of the Crimea" immortalized by Henry Wadsworth Longfellow's "Lady of the Lamp." (It was Florence Nightingale who was responsible for the success of "pavilion" hospitals.) Hospital Day was also "open house" and thousands visited Methodist Hospital to marvel at the efficiency and modern equipment of a sparkling and well run hospital.

In common with the turn of the century campaign when *The Good Samaritan* served as the campaign organ, a new publication, *Methodist Hospital News* was initiated. Well written and well edited, the publication focused on various departments of the hospital along with news stories and editorials urging support for the drive to raise a million dollars. One editorial is worth quoting in part: "Many times recently Methodist Hospital has been referred to as 'Everybody's Hospital'. It is just that. To persons of all creeds, to the wealthy, to persons of modest means and to persons of no means at all, it offers modern hospital care." It could have added, "at low cost rates" for hospital costs were fixed at $2.50 a day in the wards, $5 a day for semi-private rooms and $7 a day for a private room. (Hotel rates at that time ranged from $1 to $5 a day).

There was, however, one big difference between the 1929 campaign and that of the turn of the century. Two new mediums were available: radio and the motion picture. Arthur Baxter, campaign chairman, appeared regularly on local radio stations and "The Methodist Hospital Good Will Program" was broadcast weekly on Thursday nights at eight o'clock on WFBM. The program used some of the best musical talent in the city and each week spotlighted a department of the hospital. A film, "New Armor," produced by H.H. Coburn, was shown before groups of campaign workers and civic, social, fraternal and patriotic groups. Its cost was underwritten by "a friend of the hospital." Playing the leading role in the movie was Miss Valencia Meng, a student at Butler University.

METHODIST HOSPITAL NEWS

A Bulletin Published in the Interest of the Expansion Program Now Under Way at This Great Institution of Healing

VOLUME I INDIANAPOLIS, INDIANA, MAY 27, 1929 FIRST ISSUE

Launch Appeal for Expansion Fund

NEW UNITS OFFER OPPORTUNITY TO SELECT MEMORIAL

Many of City's Honored Names Expected to be Enshrined Here

WIDE RANGE IN COST

Establishment of memorials has an instant appeal. Men and women are turning to things outside their own lives, outside their own homes and families and businesses to build that which will carry on their influence, or to perpetuate the memory of those they have loved.

Because of the deep, inward satisfaction which results from the creation of a memorial that will go on through the years ministering to suffering humanity, it is expected that there will be a great massing of memorials in the new units of the Indianapolis Methodist Hospital.

The tendency today is to establish these memorials at home, where they will help the men and women who have worked for us or worked with us toward better health and happier lives. In this community there have been many honored names associated with the city's development, and it is expected that a great number of these

(Continued on Page Two)

MORE ROOM FOR MATERNITY CASES

Department to Be One of the Most Modern in Central States

One of the features of the new Service Unit of the Methodist Hospital which will have a wide appeal is the new maternity department. Last year 753 babies were born in this institution, and the number would have been doubled if facilities had been available to meet all the demands for admittance. The hospital has been forced to turn away maternity patients every

BAXTER WILL HEAD FUND APPEAL

Arthur R. Baxter

Arthur R. Baxter, one of the leading business men of Indianapolis, and first vice-president of the board of trustees of the Methodist Hospital, will serve as chairman of the expansion fund appeal.

Mr. Baxter is one of the institution's most loyal supporters and his acceptance of the chairmanship of the present movement insures a capable, resourceful, and energetic leader.

Under Mr. Baxter's leadership, an organization will be built up to carry the expansion fund appeal to the civic-minded and philanthropic citizens of Indianapolis.

ENVIABLE RECORD IN GIVING ANESTHETICS

An enviable record has been made by the Department of Anesthesia at the Methodist Hospital, under the capable direction of Dr. Marie B. Kast, assisted by four specially trained physicians.

A total of 5,146 general anesthetics was administered by the department last year, without a single accident.

NEW SURGERY WILL CONTAIN 27 ROOMS

More Than 6,000 Cases Cared For Last Year by Department

One of the outstanding features of the Methodist Hospital expansion program is the enlarged and thoroughly modernized Surgical Department, which will occupy an entire floor of the new Service Building. The new department will occupy 27 rooms.

More than 6,000 surgical cases were cared for last year by this department, which is under the direction of Miss Martha MacDougall, general supervisor, and four assistants.

The new surgery contains 18 operating rooms, arranged to take care of the surgical work in two main divi-

(Continued on Page Three)

Weather Forecast

NEED $1,000,000 FOR ADDITIONS TO HOSPITAL PLANT

Announcement Made At Dinner For Indianapolis Business and Civic Leaders

DR. DURANT IS GUEST

Announcement of an appeal for an expansion fund of one million dollars for the Indianapolis Methodist Hospital was made by Arthur R. Baxter, vice-president of the board of trustees of the institution, at a dinner held at the Columbia Club on Monday evening, May 27th, attended by business and civic leaders of the city.

Three new units—the new Service Building, now nearing completion, the 200-bed unit now under construction, and the new Nurses' Home—are included in the hospital's expansion program, Mr. Baxter said.

Erection of the new Service Building marks one of the most important milestones in the hospital's development, he declared. Among the facilities which the new building will provide are modern and adequate quarters for the new surgery, new laboratories provided with the latest equipment, new X-ray rooms equipped with the latest apparatus, new maternity department, and examination, treatment and work rooms. It will make possible a type of service unequalled in the Middle West.

More Beds Needed

The new 200-bed unit will contain comfortable private rooms, three, four, five, six, and seven bed wards, diet kitchens, floor laboratories, and a roof garden. Addition of the new unit will help to provide Indianapolis with the number of beds deemed necessary for adequate hospitalization. Indianapolis now is nearly 400 beds short of the number required to meet the desired ratio of five beds per thousand population. This ratio has been fixed by medical and hospital authorities as important not only for normal operation, but also to care for emergencies.

The third unit included in the expansion program is the new Jacob E. Wile Nurses' Home, which provides

An appeal for a million dollar expansion fund was featured in the first issue of Methodist Hospital News, May 27, 1929.

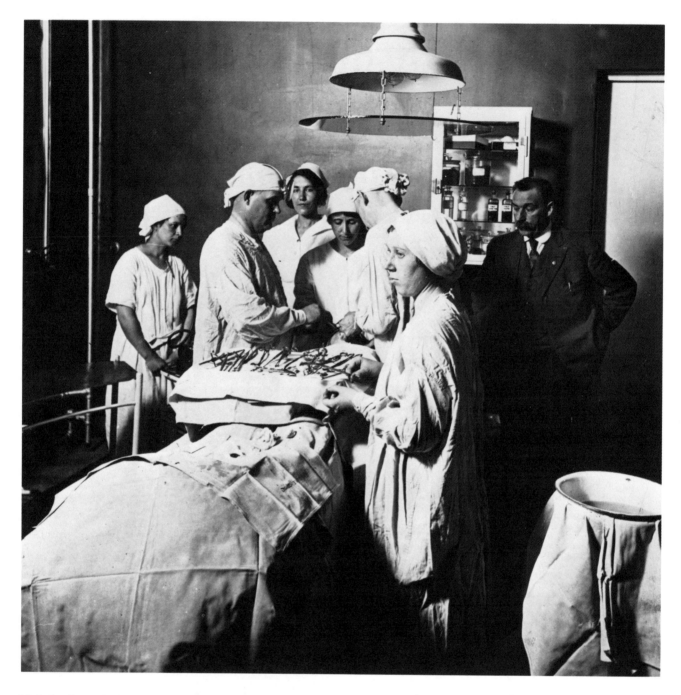

Methodist Hospital's Operating Room, 1921. The surgical team performing a tonsilectomy are — left to right: Unknown, Dr. C.H. McCaskey, Martha Emhardt, R.N., Dr. Marie Kast Kuhlman, anesthetist, Dr. J. Kent Leasure, Lula Owen, unknown.

Dr. Will Durant of New York, author, historian and philosopher, came to town as the principal speaker for the campaign's kick-off dinner in the Columbia Club. Noting that in no other age in history had there been as many philanthropists, he declared, "We tend to regard the accumulation of money and power as an ultimate end. It is not the end. It is the means. The great philanthropists realize this and are aiding in the fight against disease which for so long has been the conquerer of man."

Knute Rockne, nationally known football coach of Notre Dame's "Fighting Irishmen" football team, gave his support to the Methodist Hospital campaign. Speaking at the Columbia Club before 150 leading physicians and surgeons, hospital staff and members of the Board of Trustees, he emphasized the value of teamwork. He said in part,

"Teamwork, all important on the football field, is equally essential in the complex duties of life and in carrying forward the great projects which make communities better places in which to live. In football there must be eleven men who feel a sense of responsibility to their team and to their university who will work together to bring about a common victory. The attention of the spectator, unfortunately, is usually fastened on the men who carry the ball. They do the spectacular work and receive the applause of the stands. But the other men who interfere and tackle and block must function perfectly or the ball carrier will never get beyond the line of scrimmage. The same situation applies to community life. There are chores to be performed, menial tasks to be done. Only by every man doing his best in the particular task assigned to him can the creation of great plants such as you contemplate at Methodist Hospital here be carried out."

The city's Protestant churches also rallied to support the campaign. The weekly bulletin of the Meridian Heights Presbyterian Church provided an example. Its issue dated June 2, 1929 said, "When the new addition now going up is completed we will have one of the greatest hospitals of the country. At present there are only two other hospitals in America which rival us in X-ray equipment. We say 'Us.' We are proud of this great Protestant hospital. It has been called, 'Everybody's Hospital.' For some years it has given annually about $120,000 in service to those unable to pay and discounts without regard to their religious affiliation. We will back it."

As with other campaigns, gifts, subscriptions, memorials and endowments were solicited. An entire floor, reported *The Methodist Hospital News*, could be selected for a memorial at a cost ranging from $40,000 to $125,000. Other memorials could be secured for as little as $500, $750, and $1,000.

The largest campaign gift, however, was unsolicited and voluntary; that of Mrs. Mary Hanson Carey, who in July of 1929 gave the hospital $500,000 with the stipulation that $300,000 was to be used for the building fund in honor of her father, Julius A. Hanson, a prominent Indianapolis businessman and for 38 years director and vice president of the Belt Railroad and Stock Yards Company. In making the gift, Mrs. Carey fulfilled a wish that her father had expressed in life to assist in some philanthropic work that would benefit and

Shown here is Jacob E. Wile for whom Wile Hall was named and dedicated on November 8, 1928 as a residence and classroom facilities for the Methodist Hospital School of Nursing. Mr. and Mrs. John W. Wile of Thorntown, Indiana gave $200,000 to help this dream come true and to memorialize his father. Jacob Wile's grandson, the Reverend Robert W. Fribley, would later serve as a member of the Board of Trustees and a great granddaughter, Nancy J. Fribley, would benefit from this generous gift as a student in the DePauw School of Nursing, class of 1964.

help mankind.

Mrs. Carey, the widow of Samuel S. Carey, stipulated the remaining $200,000 was a personal gift to the hospital laboratory in the form of an endowment fund, the interest to be spent annually "upon research work and the solving of medical problems that may arise." The fund would be known as the Mary Hanson Carey Foundation for Research and administered by Mrs. Carey, Arthur Brown, president of the Board of Trustees, and Mrs. Carey's physician, Dr. David L. Kahn.

Other substantial gifts followed including $60,000 from the family of Thomas Taggart for construction of a fifth floor children's ward and solarium. Taggart, a former Indianapolis mayor and U.S. Senator, was for many years a powerful force in the Democratic party and known as the "Tammany of the Middle West." A $15,000 gift from Mrs. John J. Appel and her son, Fred G. Appel, a prominent real estate and insurance man, was donated as a perpetual endowment to provide hospital care for "newsboys and other needy children."

Methodist Hospital was not without its philanthropists.

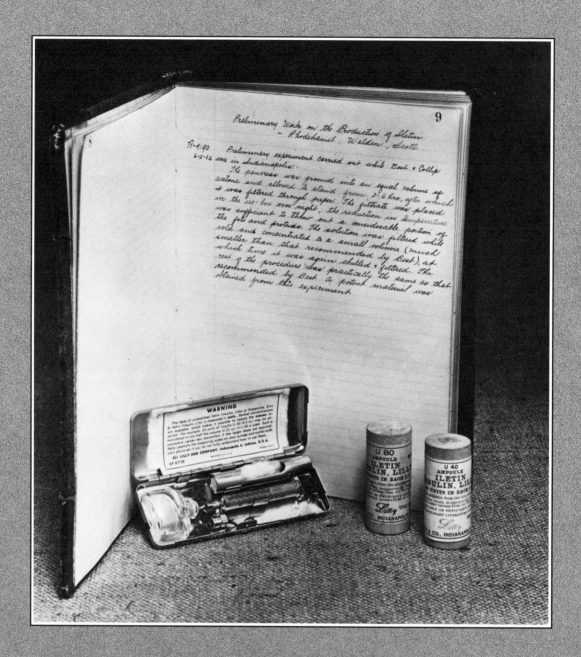

Chapter Six

Making Medical History

> *"It is doubtful if there has ever been a medical discovery comparable in drama to the effect of the administration of those precious vials of insulin when they became available . . ."*
> —Sir Derrick Dunlop,
> pharmacological scholar,
> writing in *Medicines In Our Times*

A 1922 Eli Lilly and Company laboratory notebook detailing an experiment as part of its preliminary work on the production of insulin. Shown here is a glass syringe used to inject the insulin as well as containers of Lilly's trademarked Itelin, the first commercially manufactured insulin for diabetes. (Photo courtesy Eli Lilly and Company)

In the 1920s Methodist Hospital played an important role in a dramatic and historic medical breakthrough—the use of insulin in the treatment of diabetes mellitus. It was a breakthrough that meant life for untold millions all over the world for, up to that time, a diagnosis of diabetes was akin to receiving a sentence of death.

Diabetes had plagued humankind for centuries and, in fact, had been diagnosed as early as 1,500 years before the birth of Christ. Aretaeus had coined the word in 2 A.D., an Ionic Greek word meaning "to run through a syphon." Other ancient doctors noted the disease and recorded its symptoms and complications. In succeeding centuries, it was called "Madhumeha" or "honey urine." Later, the Latin word, "mellitus," meaning honey, was applied.

In the nineteenth century, Brockman in his study of fish, and Langorhans in his study of humans, described clusters of cells present in the pancreas which they referred to as small islands in a sea of pancreatic tissue. In 1889 two German scientists, Minkowski and von Mereing, noted that if the pancreas were removed from an animal it developed diabetes. Later studies found that even if the pancreas were destroyed and the islets preserved, the animals did not become diabetic.

Meanwhile, doctors who had recognized diabetes as the inablility of the body to control blood sugars, relied on near starvation diets and exercise programs. The diets usually consisted of high fat and low carbohydrates and lived up to the old cliche about the "cure being worse than the complaint." At least one doctor recalls that at Methodist Hospital diabetic meals consisted of some unappetizing "black looking stuff" served in special crocks.

Dr. Frederick G. Banting (right) and his assistant, Charles Best, conducted experiments which led to the use of insulin for the control of diabetes. Dr. Banting and another physician, Dr. J.R.R. McLeod, were awarded the Nobel Prize for their work. Banting, who believed McLeod's role did not merit sharing the prize, split his money with Best. McLeod divided his award with Charles Collip, a young biochemist.

It was against this backdrop of limited medical knowledge that a thirty year old Canadian surgeon, Dr. Frederick G. Banting, of Toronto, began to pursue the idea that the pancreas might be the key to finding a way to treat diabetes. He discussed his idea with J.R.R. McLeod, head of the physiology department of the University of Toronto, and outlined a planned experiment: to close off the pancreatic ducts of an animal, wait for the pancreas to shrink, then isolate and extract the insulin. A skeptical McLeod gave Banting eight dogs, a student assistant, Charles Best (chosen over another senior student by the flip of a coin), and laboratory space for experimenting. McLeod then headed for Scotland for some fishing and grouse shooting.

Banting and Best worked on a shoestring budget. They tended the dogs themselves and, as

no other laboratory animals were available to test their crude extracts for toxicity, they tested it on each other. Although their first experiments were encouraging, the initial injections were painful, caused abscesses, and led only to a modest drop of blood sugar. Help was provided by Charles Collip, a young biochemist and an expert in extraction methods. McLeod, in the meantime, returned from Scotland and joined the experimenters. By the end of 1921 they were prepared to try their lifesaving extract on a human diabetic. On January 11, 1922 they injected their experimental insulin in a critically ill fourteen-year old boy and saved his life. Treatment of diabetes had become a reality.

In December of 1921, a few weeks before the first insulin shot was administered, Banting and Best lectured on their experiments at New Haven, Connecticut. Among those in the audience was George Henry Alexander Clowes, head of the research staff of Eli Lilly and Company, Indianapolis. Clowes was excited over the findings. After the lecture he talked with Banting and Best and advised them that in order to purify and stabilize their insulin and make it available in sufficient quantities, vast resources would be required. The Eli Lilly Company, he told them, was willing to collaborate.

At first the University of Toronto held back, but by May of 1922, it concluded outside help was needed and signed an agreement with Lilly. The Lilly Company immediately committed $250,000 to the joint effort, gave the fledgling insulin the brand name Iletin, and mobilized its resources to find a way to purify and stabilize the insulin derived from the pancreas of cows and hogs.

The first units of Lilly manufactured insulin were given to patients in August of 1922 at Methodist and Boston hosptials. By prearrangement, and some inter-medical politics, the first shot was administered in Boston to a Miss Elizabeth Mudge by Dr. Elliott P. Joslin, a leading diabetologist of the day (whose Joslin Clinic is now world famous).

At the same time, the first of the Lilly made insulin was administered to its first patient at Methodist Hospital by Mrs. Ruth Michael Warvel, R.N., under the direction of her husband, Dr. John H. Warvel, chief of laboratory services and Methodist Hospital's first full time pathologist. (Dr. Warvel, a graduate of the medical school at Ohio State, and Miss Michael, a graduate of the

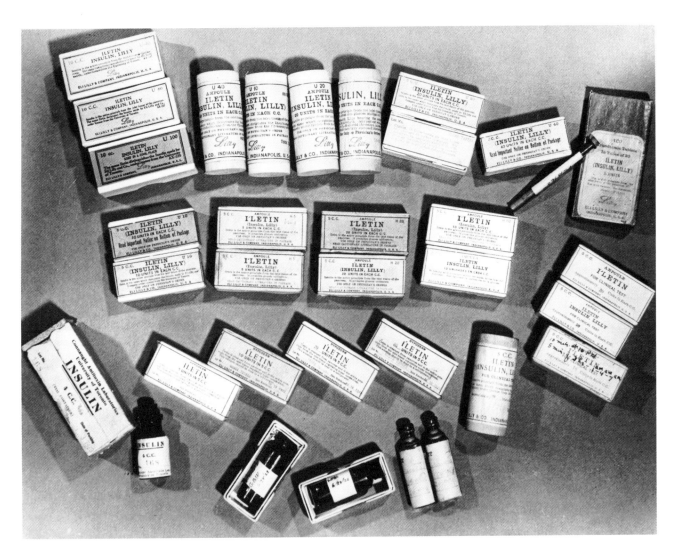

A display of early insulin packaging by Eli Lilly and Company of Indianapolis and the Connaught Antitoxin Laboratories, University of Toronto.

Methodist Hospital School of Nursing, had been wed the preceding September.) The recipient of the initial insulin shot was Mrs. Nellie Underwood of Indianapolis, a member of the Methodist Hospital housekeeping staff. Two other diabetic patients received insulin on that historic day, but, unfortunately, their identities are not known. None of the three, it was reported, experienced any side effects and went on to lead productive lives.

The first Lilly insulin, U-10, came in a glass vial with a rubber stopper and was given by way of a glass syringe. Because no one knew what reactions might develop, Mrs. Warvel recalls that patients were closely watched around the clock and pulse, temperature and blood pressure were taken every half hour plus regular tests for sugar in the blood

Lilly insulin finishing line (1923) (Photo courtesy Eli Lilly and Company)

Dr. John H. Warvel, Sr. supervised the injection of the first commercially produced insulin at Methodist Hospital in August of 1922. The Lilly-manufactured insulin was administered by his wife, the former Ruth Michael, a registered nurse. Dr. Warvel became one of the early specialists in the treatment of diabetes and, with others, paved the way for Methodist becoming a recognized center for the treatment of diabetes. (Photo courtesy of Mrs. John H. Warvel, Sr.)

and urine. These tests, in 1922, were primitive as well as time consuming. Urine was tested in blue Fehling's solution heated in a teaspoon held over a lighted candle, and blood by way of the Folin-Wu Test which involved cooking for 30 minutes and

The restored medical chart cart above was used by Dr. John H. Warvel, Sr. His son, who followed in his medical footsteps, would ride in the bottom of the cart, as a small child, as Dr. Warvel made rounds. The cart is still in use on the diabetic unit.

filtering for another 15. Today both tests require but a few minutes.

Lacking modern monitoring equipment, doctors and nurses were on the constant alert for "visible signs" of a change in a patient's condition or side effects. (There is a saying in the pharmaceutical business, "Show me a drug without side effects and I'll show you a drug without any effect.") This close patient watch led to at least one incident. Mrs. Warvel tells the story of the day her husband visited a female diabetic whom he suspected might have hyperglycemia or high blood sugar, a condition which produces an acetone or sweet fruity odor on the breath. As Dr. Warvel leaned over the patient's bed to sniff for the tell-tale sign, the woman, obviously mistaking the good doctor's intentions, raised her head slightly and kissed him full on the lips.

As a result of Methodist's pioneering efforts, doctors from all over the country came to Indianapolis to talk with Dr. Warvel, visit his patients, and stop in at the Lilly plant. Many came to plead for the precious life saving insulin. Among the visitors to Methodist Hospital were Banting and Best who conferred with Dr. Warvel and examined his meticulously kept records. In the meantime, other hospitals began experimenting with the new commercially produced insulin and Methodist became one of ten regional hospitals where insulin

This 1929 photo of the laboratory shows Dr. Horace M. Banks direct-ing a test. He stressed the use of laboratory techniques in aiding staff physicians to determine the pathology of patients in the hospital as well as more basic research "which will enable science to make ad-ditional conquests of diseases which long have taken a heavy toll of human life."

was available on a limited test basis. Records show that during the 1922-1923 period, before Lilly placed insulin on the market in late 1923, Methodist Hospital treated 135 diabetic patients. A special diabetic ward and a clinic were established under the supervision of Drs. John A. MacDonald and C.L. Rudesill.

Dr. MacDonald would remember that "in the management of these patients we encountered every known complication of diabetes and some that were unknown prior to that time, for, due to our lack of experience and, to some extent, to the variation in insulin potency, we had not infrequent instances of insulin shock or hyperinsulinism." Dr. MacDonald could also report that Methodist Hospital was the first to recognize insulin hypoglycemia in latent coronary sclerosis. The identification of diabetes as a unitary disease also paved the way for a new and important area of medical study, endocrinology.

The use of insulin meant a change in diabetic diets. Dr. Warvel was among the first to advocate a carefully weighed diet; that is, the weighing of food so that patient intake was in precise amounts and in balance with insulin. He had little patience with those who failed to follow his instructions. His son, Dr. John H. Warvel, Jr. (like his father an internist specializing in diabetes) remembers his father would simply "throw patients out of the office" with the feisty comment, "You're just wasting your money and my time and I'll have none of it."

Dr. Warvel, his son recalled, began to divide his time between Methodist Hospital's laboratory and Lilly's as he became more and more deeply involved with the use and development of insulin—even helping Lilly respond to the mountains of correspondence which the discovery of insulin had triggered. He also had the ability to quickly calculate dosage, timing and diet so necessary for the control of diabetes. Usually a time consuming process involving intricate calculations, Dr. Warvel, according to his son "could accomplish in days what it took others weeks, and it was uncanny how he always came out right."

Methodist Hospital was the scene of yet another pioneering medical development in the 1920s—development of treatment for pernicious anemia, which claimed untold thousands of victims each year. Pernicious anemia is caused by an increased production of red blood cells that are structurally abnormal and have attenuated life spans. Generally the cause is the body's inability to absorb vitamin B-12.

Working in close cooperation with scientists from Eli Lilly and Company, Methodist doctors helped work out the problem by applying specific properties found in the livers of cattle. In the 1930s pernicious anemia, like diabetes, was under control and Methodist Hospital again had the proud distinction of being an important contributor in the development of a treatment destined to save countless thousands of lives.

There were footnotes to the story of insulin.

Drs. Banting and McLeod were awarded the Nobel Prize for the discovery of insulin. Banting, who believed that McLeod's role did not merit sharing the prize, split his prize money with Best. McLeod, in turn, divided his award with Collip.

The manufacture of insulin revolutionized Lilly's position in the pharmaceutical industry and, in the words of J.K. Lilly, Sr., put the firm "on the way to present and future greatness." By 1936 Lilly's

The Rev. Demetrious Tillotson, superintendent of Methodist Hospital in 1922. A graduate of DePauw University, Greencastle, and the Garrett Biblical Institute, Chicago, he was formerly president of the Northwest Methodist Conference and superintendent of the South Bend and Crawfordsville Districts. Earlier he had served as pastor of Methodist churches in Lebanon, Lafayette, Terre Haute and Greencastle. He resigned as superintendent of Methodist Hospital to become superintendent of the Presbyterian Hospital, Denver, Colorado. (Photo courtesy of Dr. Tillotson's daughter, Mrs. Joe McCord.)

world-wide distribution necessitated the printing of 273 different labels. In 1975 the company was using a ton of fresh animal pancreas every hour in its insulin manufacturing operation.

Dr. Warvel resigned his post at Methodist Hospital in 1925 to go into full-time private practice specializing in metabolic medicine. He continued, however, to work with the hospital. Before his death, he contracted diabetes and, although his was a mild case, he opted to take regular insulin shots.

And Methodist Hospital, by virtue of its pioneering effort, continuing research and clinical application, became nationally recognized as an important center for the treatment of diabetes.

Chapter Seven

Barter, Debt, and Change

> *The luxury of doing good surpasseth every other personal enjoyment.*
> —Motto,
> White Cross Guild

With the opening on May 12, 1930 of the Julius A. Hanson Memorial Unit, Methodist Hospital, Indianapolis, became the largest and best equipped Methodist hospital in the world. And its new capacity of 635 beds, according to the American Hospital Association, placed it among the six largest hospitals in the United States.

The new unit marked the fifth major addition to the hospital since its opening in 1908. The other four, proudly listed in the *Methodist Hospital News*, included the Mary S. Yount Pavilion, opened in 1913; the north wing in 1916; the west wing in 1921 and a five-story service building which housed the clinical laboratories, X-ray, maternity and surgical departments. Not included was the Jacob E. Wile Memorial Nurses' Home, a part of the hospital complex but standing apart a short distance north of the hospital. Each unit in its own way, was a monument not only to the philanthropy of the wealthy, but to thousands of people from all faiths and all walks of life. It was with good reason that Methodist Hospital was called "the people's hospital."

Distinguished Protestant ministers and laymen were among those attending the dedication ceremonies for the new Julius A. Hanson Unit. The dedicatory speaker was the Reverend Ernest C. Wareing, D.D., editor of *The Western Christian Advocate*, Cincinnati, Ohio. Indiana Governor Harry G. Leslie and Indianapolis Mayor Reginald Sullivan extended greetings and Arthur R. Baxter, chairman of the building committee, formally presented the new building to the presiding officer, Arthur V. Brown, chairman of the Board of Trustees. The Reverend George M. Smith, hospital superintendent, proudly unlocked the doors of the building and declared it open to the public.

Methodist Hospital's famous beacon under construction. The 80-foot tower, rising 285 feet above the ground, was formally dedicated on November 9, 1933. It was a gift of Mary Hanson Carey.

The new Julius A. Hanson Memorial Unit.

Mary Hanson Carey

One of Methodist Hospital's most generous friends of another era was Mary Hanson Carey, the widow of Samuel S. Carey. In July of 1929 she gave the hospital $500,000 with the stipulation $300,000 would be used for the building fund in honor of her father, Julius A. Hanson. The other $200,000 was a personal gift to the hospital laboratory in the form of an endowment fund to be known as the Mary Hanson Carey Foundation for Research. In 1933 Mrs. Carey provided funds for the Mary Hanson Carey Memorial Chapel and a new lobby including men's and women's lounges. In the same year she provided for the construction of the hospital's most famous landmark, the Lighthouse of Health Beacon atop the hospital. (Photo courtesy of Dr. and Mrs. Vincent B. Alig)

Visitors were lavish in their praise of the new unit with its wide, airy corridors, diet kitchens, service rooms and large, cheerful patient rooms. Singled out for special attention was the fifth floor memorial to Thomas A. Taggart, which was assigned as a children's floor. The special floor with its vitaglass solarium and fountain extended over the passageway between the new unit and the old hospital and was made possible by a gift from Mrs. Taggart, the widow and her children in memory of U.S. Senator Thomas Taggart. *The Indianapolis News* provided the following glowing description:

"The Taggart Memorial children's floor with its solarium and airy rooms has become the delight of the hospital staff. Something entirely different in the way of decorations and furnishings for a children's hospital has been constructed through the assistance of Miss Lucy Taggart, who designed separate color schemes for each

room. With rose, lavender, sea green, mauve, mulberry, pink and other delicate shades, the ordinarily drab hospital rooms have been transformed into cheerful play rooms. Cubical arrangements for groups of beds and private rooms all have been treated differently and not a corner is hidden from the sunlight."

The year following the opening of the Hanson Unit, B Building, brought a changing of the guard as the Reverend George M. Smith, superintendent since 1923, resigned from his heavy and increasing responsibilities and was succeeded by yet another Methodist minister, the Reverend Dr. John G. Benson, for the past seven years superintendent of the White Cross Hospital of Columbus, Ohio, where he had established an enviable record for hospital administration. Dr. Benson, a graduate of DePauw University and the Boston University School of Theology, assumed his new duties in April of 1931 at a salary of $7,500 a year. The

Reverend Smith was named the first "Superintendent Emeritus" reflecting the esteem in which he was held by the Board of Trustees.

There were other personnel changes. Mrs. Margaret Marlowe, administrative dietitian since the hospital's beginning 22 years before, resigned and was replaced by Miss Verna Ansorge. The X-ray department also got a new head, Dr. Harold C. Ochsner. He succeeded Dr. Arthur C. Echternacht, who had headed the unit since 1926 and designed the X-ray department in the new unit. Dr. Ochsner, a graduate of the University of Minnesota, took a leave of absence from 1933 to 1937 for further training at the Mayo Clinic. During his absence, the department was in the charge of Drs. Bernard D. Harrington, E. Lee Shiflet and Bernard Kalyjan.

The X-ray department, like the laboratory, was one of the hospital's fastest growing departments because of its increasing importance in the diagnosis and treatment of patients. Advances in the recognition and treatment of pneumonia, for instance, demanded the finest of X-ray facilities. In this respect, Methodist was always in the fore-

front. It was among the first to install state-of-the-art equipment such as the machine installed in 1938 that took pictures in one-fortieth of a second and was rated as one of the most powerful in the United States. By 1938, Dr. Ochsner could report that the department was handling 9,000 diagnostic and 3,000 treatment cases annually.

Other personnel and administrative changes followed. Clarence C. Hess was appointed business manager and purchasing agent and later controller. A personnel division was established. Miss Fannie R. Forth was named superintendent of nurses and director of the School of Nursing after being transferred from Gary Hospital where she had held a similar position. The nursing school was placed on a strictly academic basis "to harmonize with the program at DePauw University" and tuition fees were fixed at $50 a year. A new department of social services and statistics was organized by Richard B. Benson, son of the superintendent. The younger Benson served only briefly, accepting a position in 1933 as business manager of Methodist Hospital in Omaha, Nebraska. A new method of filing individual

A vitaglass solarium was a feature of the children's floor of the Julius A. Hanson unit opened in 1930. Located on the fifth floor, it was a memorial to Senator Thomas A. Taggart and made possible by Taggart's widow and children. The building was the gift of Mrs. Mary Hanson Carey in honor of her father, Julius A. Hanson, prominent Indianapolis businessman.

medical records of patients was installed in 1932 with the approval of the American Hospital Association, the American Medical Association and the American College of Surgeons. Mrs. Mabel Ellen Tracy, a graduate of Indiana University, was appointed to head up the medical records library. The system was to play a significant role in upgrading and maintaining a high standard of medical care. The name of the hospital also underwent a change: it was no longer the Methodist Episcopal Hospital of Indiana, but Methodist Hospital of Indiana, the name reflecting the 1939 merger of the Methodist Episcopal Church, Methodist Episcopal Church South, and the Methodist Protestant Church. And because "some patients were complaining of being annoyed by

Second woman doctor to join the Methodist Hospital staff was Dr. Marie Kast, a graduate of the Indiana University School of Medicine, Dr. Kast joined the Methodist staff in 1916 and practiced anesthesiology. Before coming to Methodist she had been house physician at the Robert Long Hospital.

lawyers against the advice of attending physicians," agents, solicitors and lawyers were banned from visiting patients.

From the beginning Methodist Hospital had admitted women doctors to its staff. The first woman doctor at Methodist was Dr. Lillian B. Mueller, a 1909 graduate of Indiana University School of Medicine, who joined the Methodist staff in 1910 after serving briefly as house physician at Women's Hospital, Detroit. Dr. Mueller served until 1919 when she left Methodist to pursue post-graduate studies at the New York Post Graduate School. The second woman to join the medical staff was Dr. Marie B. Kast (later Mrs. H. Theodore Kuhlman), also a graduate of Indiana University, class of 1913. She came to Methodist Hospital in 1916 after serving as house physician at the Robert W. Long Hospital, Indianapolis. Both doctors practiced anesthesiology and are credited with a long and proud record of accident-free anesthetizations. Dr. Mueller was said to be the first to introduce gas anesthesia to Methodist Hospital. In later years she opened an office in the American Central Life Insurance Building for the practice of otorhinolaryngology (ear, nose and throat.)

In 1932 a hotel department was established on the main floor of the west wing with Mrs. Esther Fraser of Princeton, Indiana in charge. The hotel was opened, along with a tea room, in order "that relatives or other guests of patients might have pleasant overnight accommodations at reasonable cost under the same roof and within a moment's call." Guests of the hotel included convalescent patients as well as patients undergoing observation and tests.

Three other departments were opened later in the same year—a pharmacy managed by Paul D. Brown; a barber shop operated by Harry N. Crook; and a beauty parlor operated by Mrs. Crook. Although these units were installed for the use of patients, they were also open to the public. Profits from the stores and shops were applied to the fund for free patient service.

The year 1933 brought into being an important symbol and service consistent with the dreams of the founders—the Mary Hanson Carey Memorial Chapel, planned and donated by Mrs. Carey as a memorial to her parents, Julius A. and Belle M. Hanson. Designed for the use of Protestant, Jewish and Catholic faiths, it incorporated the symbols of each religion and, in a very real sense, represented Methodism's traditional principle of promoting cooperation and better understanding among the different religions. This ecumenical approach was as old as the church, extending back to John Wesley, who once said, "the world is my parish."

Dedication of the chapel and a new lobby including men's and women's lounges—also a gift of Mrs. Carey—was in the charge of a committee headed by Mrs. Carey's pastor, Dr. Jean S. Milner, pastor of the Second Presbyterian Church. Other committee members included Rabbi Morris Feuerlicht, Dr. W.C. Hartinger, and Dr. Ernest N. Evans of the church federation. The memorial was presented officially by Dr. W.W. Wyatt of the

The first woman member of Methodist Hospital's Medical Staff was Dr. Lillian B. Mueller, shown here with anesthesia equipment in this 1916 photograph. Dr. Mueller, a 1909 graduate of Indiana University Medical School, served as the hospital's anesthesiologist from 1910 to 1919 when she left to pursue post graduate studies in New York.

North Methodist Episcopal Church.

Two of the most beautiful features of the new chapel were imported from Italy—a 150 year old baptismal font and a reproduction of Thornwaldsen's famous sculpture, "Serving Christ," executed in white Carrara marble. Transportation for the statue was paid by the Italian government when it learned the sculpture was to be placed in an American hospital.

In the same year, 1933, yet another splendid gift of Mrs. Carey was dedicated—the hospital's most famous landmark, the Lighthouse of Health Beacon atop the hospital. Believed to be the first of its kind in the United States, the beacon was patterned after the famous lighthouse at the Royal Hospital of St. Bartholomew, London, whose light had served as a beacon of hope since 1857. Before the Methodist beacon could be built, an agreement was negotiated with the federal government that provided the beacon be lighted around the clock not only as a guide to flyers, but to warn off low flying planes. The beacon light was turned on for the first time on the evening of November 9, 1933 at dedication ceremonies on the roof garden of the Nurses' Home. Using a remote control device, the beacon was lighted by Bishop Edgar Blake of the Detroit Area and the Reverend Dr. Milner. Designed to let the world know, "this is a haven of health," the beacon was formally dedicated "to the servants of religion, who would serve the sick; to the servants of medical science, who would serve humanity; and to the servants of philanthropy, who would live for others."

Participating in the dedication services were Dr. William N. Wishard, Sr., who spoke on, "The Ideals of the Medical Profession and the Modern Hospital;" Dr. Harry B. Gouch, DePauw University; Alden B. Mills, editor, *Modern Hospital*; Maxine Pemberton, graduate nurse, Methodist Hospital; Albert G. Hahn, president, Indiana Hospital Association; Dr. N.E. Davis, secretary, Board of Hospitals, Methodist Church; Sister Mary Reginald, president, Indiana Catholic Hospital Association; Matthew O. Foley, editor, *Hospital Management*; Indianapolis Mayor Reginald Sullivan; Reverend W.W. Wyatt, secretary, Board of Trustees; Dr. E.D. Clark, chairman, Medical Advisory Board; and Arthur V. Brown, president of the Board of Trustees. The invocation was given by the Reverend W.C. Hartinger and music was provided by the *Indianapolis News* Boys Band and Miss Fan-

The Mary Hanson Carey Memorial Chapel was designed for the use of Protestant, Catholic and Jew by Mary Hanson Carey as a memorial to her mother and father in 1933. Patients, their family members and employees use it for private prayer and public worship.

nie Kiser, harpist. Dr. Albert Hahn would later recall there were so many speakers, he didn't give his talk. "It was," he remembered, "a most gala occasion."

Mrs. Carey took a special pride in the health beacon and it was an oft told story that she would sit in the window of her luxury apartment at the Marott Hotel and train her binoculars on the beacon to be sure it was fully lighted and rotating properly. If for any reason it wasn't, hospital officials could expect a telephone call and a demand that things be made right—at once.

The 1930s also marked the formation of an organization that would play a major role in the day-to-day operation of the hospital: the White Cross Guild, an organization of women dedicated to community betterment and to the activities of Methodist Hospital. In common with other Methodist Hospital groups, the White Cross Guild was open to members of all religious faiths. It adopted as its motto: "The luxury of doing good surpasseth every other personal enjoyment."

Its founder was Mrs. Edgar Blake, wife of Bishop Blake, and the White Cross Guild grew out of the original Methodist Hospital Guild, a small group of loyal and interested women who for years had rolled bandages and sewed for the hospital. Mrs. Blake patterned the new organization after a similar one in Columbus, Ohio, where Superintendent Benson had formerly served. Dr. Benson heartily endorsed the project and lent his genius for organization. Working closely with Mrs. Blake,

66

Mrs. Benson and Mrs. William C. Hartinger, Dr. Benson set about organizing the guild. Luncheon meetings were held in Wile Hall. Mrs. Edgar Blake was made president pro-tem and Mrs. O.W. Fifer, secretary, pro-tem. On February 3, 1932 Mrs. Blake's dream came true: the White Cross Guild was formally organized with 80 charter members. By June, seven units were organized and working: Mother Guild, Broadway Methodist, St. Paul Methodist, Central Avenue Methodist, Irvington Methodist, Second Presbyterian Library Guild, and Grace Methodist.

White Cross Guild was a success from the start and its many projects offered opportunities to follow the words of John Wesley "to do all the good you can in every way you can." Projects over the years included Tiny Tim, for children whose families were in need of financial help; Hall of Fame, hospital care for needy maternity patients; Elderly Patients, those without funds; Student Nurses Loan Fund; Chaplain's Social Service Fund; the Choral Club for nurses, a library for patients and personnel; and social and athletic activities for student nurses.

Mrs. Blake became the first president of the Guild and was succeeded by Mrs. Felix McWhirter. Others who served as president during the 1930s included: Mrs. W.C. Hartinger, Mrs. Isaac Born and Mrs. John W. Noble. Presidents during the 1940s were: Mrs. Carl Ploch, Mrs. Harry L. Foreman, Mrs. D.A. Bartley and Mrs. James Crooks.

Superintendent Benson worked through the Guild to bring numerous personal services to patients such as flowers and music, cheer and entertainment.

The Guild, in cooperation with Dr. Benson, assisted in beautifying "and adding a woman's touch" to the hospital. The Guild also raised funds and collected books for the expanding hospital library (opened in February of 1934); organized a Music Guild composed of 45 singers, instrumentalists and dramatic readers under the direction of Mrs. Will C. Hitz; and staged special holiday programs for children.

The White Cross Guild and other major and minor innovations during the 1930s reflected the organizational ability and sound business judgment of the hospital's dynamic new superintendent, Dr. Benson. The first of Methodist's modern hospital administrators, he was a dedicated, hard

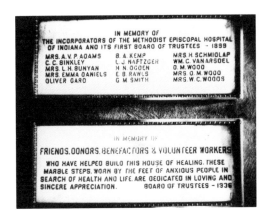

When the original steps at the hospital's front entrance were replaced in 1936, two of the well-worn steps were made into memorial tablets. Today they hang at the entrance, a tribute to friends, donors, benefactors, volunteer workers and the original incorporators and board of trustees.

working leader who quickly gained the admiration and respect of the Board of Trustees as well as the medical and nursing staffs. "He had charisma," said one of those who worked closely with him, "and he knew how to get things done."

Dr. Benson's influence extended to the Indianapolis community. He became one of the city's acknowledged civic leaders, an active member of the city's social and fraternal organizations, and one of the city's most-in-demand speakers. Newspaper reports of his many speeches would indicate that Dr. Benson was not only a man in tune with his time, but a man often in advance of the times. For instance, he spoke eloquently on such subjects as the "smog nuisance" which he called a "self imposed silly menace that costs Indianapolis citizens at least $300,000 annually in additional hospital fees"; the need for restructuring the American family; improvement of hospital facilities for Negroes and a more open approach to information on sex and social disease, all liberal ideas in the 1930s. He also advocated hospitalization insurance, condemned attempts to "socialize" medicine, and declared in a 1938 talk, many years before the word "stress" became a part of the medical vocabulary, "We are taking ourselves too seriously and it's breaking us down mentally, physically and other ways...Let's play at the game of life instead of working so hard that we are driving ourselves to nervous prostration."

A deeply religious man who believed that "religion has its therapeutical value and helps people get well," he organized a board of chaplains composed of representatives of every major religion in the city. "Disease has no denomination," Dr. Benson told an audience in Gary, Indiana. "There is no such thing as a Methodist gall bladder or a Presbyterian appendix. Our hospitals are Methodist only in the sense that the Methodist groups have undertaken the responsibility of their finances. Their doors are open to people of all races and all creeds for disease knows no social distinctions."

Methodist Hospital had long recognized the value of religion in helping patients get well and since its opening in 1908, it had been a policy to immediately notify pastors, priests and rabbis whenever one of their church or synagogue members had been admitted to the hospital. Methodist pastors regularly visited their parishioners and the superintendent personally visited patients regardless of their church affiliation. This policy continued into the 1930s even after the appointment in 1937 of the hospital's first full-time chaplain, The Reverend Dr. Charles T. Alexander. Besides serving as chaplain, Dr. Alexander, was named to the faculty of the Training School for Nurses and placed in charge of the hospital library.

Under Dr. Benson, a mid-week chapel service was inaugurated for nurses in addition to regular morning prayers and courses in Bible study. "It is the purpose of management," Dr. Benson wrote, "to give a positive Christian emphasis to all work of the hospital in addition to the emphasis on scientific discovery."

Meanwhile, the hospital, in common with other American and Indiana institutions, was feeling the effects of the Great Depression, which had been heralded by the collapse of the Bull Market on "Black Tuesday," October 29, 1929. In the beginning, bankers and business leaders remained generally optimistic and talked of the possibility of an early recovery following "a period of lowered activity." Expressions of confidence, however, were not enough. The business and economic machinery continued to break down with baffling regularity. In Indianapolis, property delinquencies doubled. University Square was filled with unemployed men. State, county and local welfare agencies were overwhelmed with demands for help. Indiana and Indianapolis found themselves torn between their log cabin individualism and the proposition that

The Rev. Dr. Charles T. Alexander, who joined Methodist Hospital as Chaplain in 1937, was the first to write a history of Methodist Hospital. His unpublished work provided the basis of other historical works.

the welfare of their people in a depression was a responsibility of government. Herbert Hoover, who had been elected in a landslide, was swept out in another. The new president, Franklin D. Roosevelt, champion of "The Forgotten Man," carried all but six Republican states and a nation sang, "Happy Days are Here Again."

The depression broke just as Methodist Hospital had completed its building program and appointed Dr. Benson as superintendent. As it became obvious that recovery wasn't just around the corner, Dr. Benson and his hard working and efficient business manager, Clarence Hess, moved to cut operating costs. All departments were alerted to scrutinize their budgets carefully and to prune all unnecessary expenses. Hess negotiated a new contract with the electric company. To cut water costs, the hospital sunk its own well. Paid vacations were abolished. On Hess' recommendations,

Dr. Benson ordered the operating budget set at $37,205 a month and departments were asked to reduce the total annual budget by $50,000. By 1935 the cost per day per patient had been reduced to $4.33. Although hospital occupancy continued to fall—at times it averaged only 200 patients a day—Dr. Benson managed to keep the hospital in the black. But the black ink was limited to the day-to-day operations. The hospital was struggling under a large capital debt, acquired in more prosperous times when optimism and philanthropy were running high. For the first time, the hospital was unable to meet payments on current interest and was forced to renegotiate the debt.

As the depression deepened, barter became the order of the day. The Indiana State Fair, for example, permitted farmers to exchange sacks of grain for tickets. In 1933 Methodist Hospital was also accepting payment of bills by way of barter. A story in *The Indianapolis News*, March 9, 1933 quoted Superintendent Benson, "Since we opened our hospital farm we have taken in hogs, chickens and farm produce as payment on hospital bills. Our latest deal was when we took 16,000 strawberry plants in payment for a bill." Emma Beaver, R.N., class of 1935, remembered that it was a hospital policy to accept payment "in kind" and that one farmer paid his account by supplying the hospital with pears. "They had them almost every day in the cafeteria," she recalled, "and even today I can hardly look a pear in the face."

But no matter how patients paid their bills, admissions for each year showed an increase. From a total of 14,143 patients admitted in 1930, the figure climbed to 17,311 in 1935 and reached over 22,000 in 1938. The hospital, however, with its more than 600 beds, was operating at a good deal less than capacity. The average occupancy in 1932 was but 258 patients; in 1933, 254 patients; in 1934, 330; and in 1935, 372 patients. It is worth noting that, while there were fewer patients, there were more charity cases; in fact, three times as many, according to Arthur V. Brown, president of the Board of Trustees writing in the May 2, 1935 edition of *The Christian Advocate.* Charity care averaged over five percent of the operating budget during the depression.

In the same article, Brown praised the management of the state's Methodist hospitals for their ability to weather the depression, despite the fact that philanthropy and other gifts had "literally

Arthur V. Brown, president of Indiana National Bank, served as president of the Methodist Hospital Board of Trustees from 1922 to 1942 — the longest tenure of any president.

frozen up." Noting that the hospitals managed to keep going without gifts and government help and with unusual charity demands to care for, Brown commented, "And strange as it may seem, at least to a businessman who is a banker (Brown was president of Indiana National Bank, Indianapolis) our hospitals have demonstrated remarkable business management to the end that they have accomplished during the depression what they had never accomplished in the days of easy prosperity; namely, balancing an operating budget."

During this same period, according to Brown, Methodist hospitals in Indiana had also reduced the costs of hospital care to the public. "Five years ago," he wrote, "the cost of hospitalization amounted to nearly $7 per day per patient. Driven by sheer necessity of existence, the management of our hospitals were not only compelled to depend on income from patients to pay expenses but compelled to reduce the cost of the care of the patient. The result is that our Indiana Methodist hospitals have an average cost per day per patient not far from $4."

Meanwhile, Dr. Benson was tangling with the city government and charging it with "unfair competition." It would not be the last time the hospital would find itself challenging the city or one of the county agencies. The controversy in the 1930s, however, revolved around City Hospital's proposal to build a new $500,000 addition to relieve crowded conditions. Dr. Benson and other Indianapolis hospital administrators were opposed to the construction, but it was Benson, acting alone, who brought the matter to a head.

In an open letter to Mayor Sullivan, which made the front page of the local newspapers, Dr. Benson said: "We appeal to you, Mr. Mayor, in this time of national emergency that no steps toward the incurring of a half million dollar indebtedness be taken for the reason that it is unnecessary. A part of our institution can be set aside to take care of City Hospital's overflow and patients can be assured of just as good care as they would receive at City.

"It is beyond our comprehension," the letter continued, "why ambulances should go screaming past private hospitals, when the patients could pay all or part of their medical expense, and be taken to the crowded City Hospital. The City Hospital, as we understand it, was built to take care of indigent cases only and to be supported by taxes from the city. This is not the prevailing policy. We witness the strange spectacle of the City Hospital entering into competition with privately supported hospitals and caring for cases at less than cost. This is manifestly unfair. Privately operated hospitals of the city already are doing a large amount of charity work and should have some protection. In this institution (Methodist) last year, the cost of free work was in excess of $100,000. So far as we are concerned," the letter concluded, "Methodist Hospital is ready to take over the entire overflow at exactly the same costs as City Hospital."

Dr. Benson's crusade against city government—launched at a time when Indianapolis' hospitals had hundreds of empty beds—proved to be successful. The proposed addition and bond issue were defeated and the city government instituted new policies to minimize competition between City

Hospital and Indianapolis' private hospitals. Everything would be fine—until the next time.

A crusade of yet another kind was launched by Dr. Benson in 1935, a crusade with the object of enlisting a quarter of a million Hoosiers who would agree to see their physician, for an annual physical examination. An early first step in what we now call preventive medicine, pledge forms were distributed to all the state's churches. In a matter of a few months, thousands had signed.

As a part of the crusade, a five-year educational campaign was launched with the object of "acquainting people with good hospitalization" and to enlist persons from all walks of life and all creeds to support "good hospitals wherever they are located." The crusade listed ten objectives which were offered as "worthy of thought...and deserving of careful and prayerful study." They were listed as follows:

1. A new interpretation of Christian hospitalization.
2. The creation of a new community understanding of the aims, purposes and needs of scientific institutional care of the sick.
3. A new patient support of all Christian hospitals.
4. The placing of hospital privileges within reach of all without pauperizing any.
5. To pledge a half million people of Indiana to see their family physicians at least once a year for a health audit.
6. Hospitalization of the mentally sick and incurables in general hospitals.
7. The removal of all indebtedness on properties of Methodist hospitals in Indiana and a continued sound operating program.
8. Establishment of nurse scholarships, which will constitute a Permanent Endowment Fund for worthy young women who wish to become nurses.
9. Support for "Tiny Tim Beds" for the care of crippled children from the homes of the poor.
10. Keeping aglow the beacon light of scientific philanthropy in the skies of Hoosier Christian thought.

The Crusade was well publicized and successful. One of the most favored objectives was number nine. "Tiny Tim" clubs proliferated all over the state. Membership in the club was $10, which provided five days of free care and hospital service for

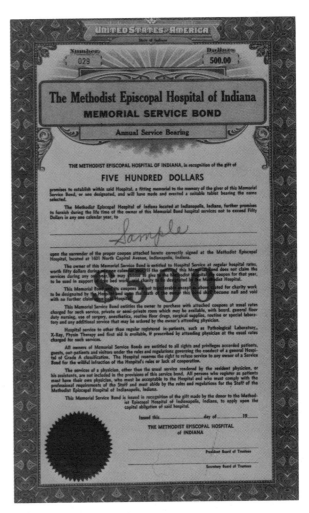

Dr. John G. Benson, superintendent of Methodist Hospital, 1931-1944. The personable, liberal and farsighted Benson was the last of several Methodist ministers to serve as superintendent. He not only guided the hospital through the trying years of the Great Depression and most of World War II, but wiped out the hospital's indebtedness.

Memorial Service Bonds, a kind of hospital insurance, were issued during the Depression years to raise funds for Indiana's Methodist Hospitals. A $500 bond, shown here, entitled the holder to $50 a year in hospitalization for ten years, a $1,000 bond, $100 for ten years. Besides promoting bonds to individuals, churches were urged to buy bonds to finance hospitalization for the needy and employers for their workers.

a crippled child. The clubs were particularly popular with Sunday School classes and church societies.

In addition to the Crusade, a "New Deal" program for Methodist Hospital was launched. It had no connection with Roosevelt's "New Deal" and was without political connotations. (In fact, Indiana's Methodist hospitals viewed with alarm the possibility of government subsidies and other forms of help as well as so-called "socialized medicine," a phrase coined by the American Medical Association in combating the possibility of government health insurance.) Actually, the Methodist program was a "New Deal in Philanthropy" and designed to raise three million dollars

in five years to pay off the institutions' capital debt which most of the hospitals, including Indianapolis' Methodist, were finding a heavy burden in a depressed economic period.

One unique and popular feature of the New Deal program was a service bond, which, in a very real sense, was a forerunner of hospital insurance—a subject widely discussed and debated in the 1930s. Designed to meet an emergency and pay off several thousand dollars in defaulted interest, the bond idea was perhaps best described in a May 8, 1934 editorial in *The Indianapolis News* which said in part:

"Hospital records show," Mr. Benson said, "that the average person needs the

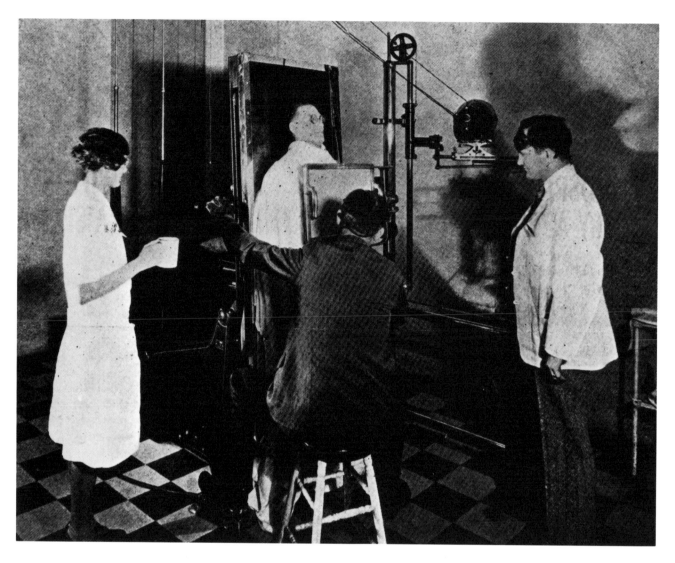

Dr. Arthur C. Echternacht, Methodist Hospital roentgenologist, using new X-ray equipment in making a gastrointestinal examination in 1929. X-ray is becoming an important part in the treatment as well as the diagnosis of disease.

services of a hospital once every ten years and that the cost is about $130. To make such an expense easier to bear, the Methodist hospitals in Indiana are issuing service bonds in denominations of $1,000 and $500. The larger bond entitles the holder to hospitalization amounting to $100 annually for ten years. Half as much is provided by the smaller bond. If the bondholder had to go to a hospital annually and his expense for each visit was not more than $100, the $1,000 bond would finance him, but the annual allowance is not cumulative and if the sums available are not used they lapse. This prompts a movement for the bond-

holder to give his 'dividend' to charity if not used.

"Bonds in denominations of $50 were explained by Dr. Benson as being suitable for some patrons. An anonymous donor has made it possible for bonds to be sold for $30 each. The holder has ten $5 coupons that may be used for hospital service at any time. Dr. Benson says that the effort is a combination of altruism and sound business principles. It is intended to aid the hospitals in avoiding deficits and to be of service to the person who, in the nature of things, will need some hospital service at times.

Another feature of the service bond not covered in the editorial was the use of bonds by churches, who were encouraged to buy bonds and use the coupons to finance hospitalization for needy families. "This will help," Dr. Benson wrote, "to locate the responsibility in our churches on the matter of caring for the free bed cases and will also help the hospital to deal fairly with all churches and their demands." Dr. Benson also suggested the purchase of bonds by employers who, of course, would use them in the case of hospitalization of their workers. To make the purchase of bonds easier, an installment payment plan was instituted. (During the 1940s bonds would be regularly presented for patient care and as late as 1984, the hospital received an inquiry concerning the validity of a bond.)

Although the Service Bond feature was popular, apparently little came of the New Deal effort for Methodist publications make no further mention of the program after its well publicized announcement in October of 1933. At Methodist Hospital, however, largely through the efforts of Superintendent Benson and the Board of Trustees headed by Arthur V. Brown, some fairly substantial gifts and endowments were obtained. Other funds became available through bequests including the will of Edmund Zoller, who left $40,000 to the hospital for a memorial.

There were also gifts of hospital equipment including the first oxygen tent donated by the Princeton (Indiana) Chapter of Psi Iota Xi. The dubious honor of being the first patient to use the tent fell to Harry Whitmore of Indianapolis. The hospital also installed two iron lungs: one full size and another for the use of a child. These were important additions in a day when polio epidemics were common. Also new at the hospital was a metal fever cabinet used to treat certain forms of syphilis and gonorrhea in the days before sulfonamides and penicillin. The cabinet replaced a dangerous practice of generating fevers by giving the patient malaria or intravenous typhoid vaccine.

On the evening of January 26, 1938 the Methodist Hospital Medical Staff (formerly the Medical Staff Society) gathered at the Claypool Hotel to honor a long time friend, Arthur V. Brown, president of the Board of Trustees since 1921 and scheduled for election to his 18th term the following day. Dr. Edmund D. Clark, a member of the original medical advisory group in 1909, representing the board and medical staff, presented Mr. Brown with a handsome scroll and declared, "The medical profession is under obligation to you and the staff is happy to express that obligation. Your work has been quietly and efficiently performed and you have contributed both interest and understanding in all the details of your long service to the hospital, the medical profession and the public."

Mr. Brown's response provided some key statistics and information about Methodist Hospital during the decade 1929 to 1939. For instance, he told the 700 assembled guests that, "Methodist Hospital and the doctors who practice there have given a total of $3,420,000 of free work to the community in the last ten years. Free service provided by the hospital totaled $1,140,000 and extended over 50,000 individuals.

"The White Cross Guild," he said, "consisted of 1,000 women, who, in 1937, donated 32,835 hours of service, which is equal to 4,104 days at eight hours a day or in terms of human life, 11 years and four months of donated service."

He also disclosed that the hospital had trained nearly 200 residents and interns during the past 10 years and nearly 1,000 women had been given nurses' training at an estimated cost of $1,960,000. Patient enrollment for the ten year period was 169,488 and 91,494 operations had been performed and 10,853 babies born during the decade.

Brown also paid tribute to the 25,000 donors who have given to the hospital throughout the years including Mrs. Mary Hanson Carey, J.K. Lilly, Sr., Mr. and Mrs. William Coleman, the family of Thomas Taggart, Delavan Smith, William E. McKee, Arthur Wolf, Fred G. Appel, Mrs. John N. Carey, Mr. and Mrs. Lucius Wainwright, and Mr. and Mrs. Louis Levey.

The tribute to Mr. Brown, which was broadcast by two local radio stations, also included a talk by Dr. J.H.J. Upham of Columbus, Ohio, president of the American Medical Association, who attributed Methodist Hospital's success "to the character of its staff and the sympathetic views of its administrative officers."

No mention was made at the dinner of two controversial issues of the 1930s which were dividing the medical and hospital communities—hospitalization insurance and "socialized" medicine. Both were favorite subjects with high school and college debaters and a principal topic of speakers before service clubs and women's groups. The Indiana State Medical Association, who opposed both, prepared a handbook for speakers and writers representing their point of view. The association also viewed with alarm any encroachment of the federal government in the area of hospitalization or medicine. A federal grant for the care of crippled children was regarded, in 1937, as a step toward state medicine.

Hospitalization insurance was one of the subjects discussed at the 15th Annual Convention of the National Methodist Association of Hospitals, Homes and Deaconess Work held at the Claypool Hotel, Indianapolis, in February of 1933. The convention, which was usually held in Chicago, had come to Indianapolis to honor Dr. Benson, retiring as national president after two terms. Methodist Hospital was also the largest of the 87 Methodist Hospitals who belonged to the prestigious association.

Although the association took no formal action on hospitalization insurance, it was a widely discussed topic at the convention. Among those

Wearing the new short-sleeved nurses' uniforms, a group of students of the Methodist Hospital School of Nursing carry out an experiment in a laboratory class in Wile Hall in 1937. Students facing camera, Left to Right are: Virginia Reed, Mary Shaw, Gay Unger, Louise Ball; others are, Left to Right: Avalon Hines, Teresa Winzinreed, Norris Ayers, and Instructor Carolyn Hoffner talking with Mae McDonald.

who spoke in favor of insurance was Paul H. Fesler, superintendent of Chicago's Wesley Hospital (now Northwestern University) and retiring president of the American Hospital Association. Noting that "it is impossible to give complete hospital care at a cost low enough for the average citizen," Fesler said, "I am in favor of an insurance plan of this sort whereby a certain amount of hospitalization may be sold to employed persons at a flat rate, on the condition that the patient may choose his hospital and his physician."

Dr. Benson, a long time advocate of hospital insurance, had brought up the subject at a meeting of the Medical Staff Society in September of 1932. The hospital superintendent recommended hospitalization insurance as a means of meeting the continuing problem of low bed occupancy. The society, after "thorough consideration," reported in January of 1933 that it was "unalterably opposed" to group hospitalization on the grounds that such plans "would lead to influences and practices in the field of both medicine and hospitalization that would be divisive and harmful and in the end bring us State Medicine, which neither the medical world nor those interested in hospitalization desire."

Meanwhile, Dr. Benson inaugurated a form of hospital insurance for Methodist Hospital employees. Known as the Fellowship Plan, it provided for deductions from employees' wages to pay for hospitalization in the event it was needed. Enrollment in the plan was a requirement for employment so it can be surmised the plan was yet another means of raising funds during the Great Depression. A similar plan was also made available to student nurses who paid $9.50 a year for group hospitalization and medical care, the hospitalization not to exceed 21 days in any 12-month period. A school physician appointed by the Board of Trustees was assigned to the student group. Student nurses, according to the school handbook, were responsible for their own dental and eye care.

The Fellowship Plan brought an immediate "condemnation" from the Executive Committee of the Indiana State Medical Association who had earlier voiced its strong opposition to the principle of group hospitalization. From their offices in the Hume Mansur Building, the association forwarded copies of a resolution adopted February 13, 1933 which read in part: "RESOLVED, that the Ex-ecutive Committee of the Indiana State Medical Association condemns group hospitalization in principle and condemns the Methodist Hospital of Indianapolis for adopting a plan which is in its essence group hospitalization..." Copies were sent to Dr. Benson, Arthur V. Brown, president of the Board of Trustees, and Dr. LaRue Carter, president of the Medical Staff Society.

As in other controversies, Dr. Benson was ahead of his time. In 1946 the Indiana State Medical Association would adopt, by unanimous vote, Articles of Incorporation of the Mutual Medical Insurance Company, a hospitalization insurance plan financed by 700 members of the association. The doctors' insurance plan would be integrated with the Blue Cross organization even to sharing the same office space and soliciting members and collecting payment.

Dr. Benson and the Medical Staff Society found themselves involved in yet another difference of opinion in 1935—this time over a new eight-hour day schedule for nurses. The eight-hour plan had been launched on a trial basis in cooperation with the Central District Nursing Association and with the understanding that other Marion County hospitals would cooperate in the experiment. As with many hospital problems, the superintendent found himself in the middle along with the nurses, who, as Dr. Benson pointed out in a memorandum, served "two masters"—the hospital that paid their salaries and the doctors who directed their activities.

The Society's position on the eight-hour day was contained in a memorandum which declared the plan "impractical and unwise" and offered eight reasons for its opposition including increased costs—"$15 a day if a special all-time attendent is required"—and the undesirability of changing nurses frequently, "particularly if the skills of the nurses might prove to be unequal."

Dr. Benson responded by proposing to set up a Division of Graduate Nursing Service which would be on a par with other administrative divisions of the hospital and under his supervision. The new division would be organized to function as a nurses' registry with rates fixed at $1.50 for the first hour and fifty cents an hour thereafter. Rates would be $5 for an eight-hour day; $6 for a 16-hour day; and $7 for a 24-hour day. Under the proposal, nurses would buy their own meals.

The eight-hour day controversy, however, became moot when Dr. Benson found that other Marion County hospitals were not cooperating and withdrew Methodist's support. "It will be administrative policy," he decreed, "to remain on the old plan until such time as there is a plan as will reveal the evident and sincere organized cooperation of the nursing profession, medical profession, and especially all of the hospitals of Marion County."

The year 1932 marked the first time that tuition was charged students of the Methodist Hospital School of Nursing. Student nurses paid tuition of $175 in 1932, $375 in 1937, and $450 in 1939. In addition, the students paid for their books, uniforms and equipment estimated at $150 for the three years. The tuition charge made the school self supporting and produced a modest profit each year, an important factor during the depression years. Besides its affiliation with DePauw University, the school in 1939 became affiliated with Butler University, Evansville College and Taylor University.

Student uniforms also underwent a change. For the first time, short sleeved gingham uniforms were permitted, replacing the long sleeved uniforms with their six and eight inch cuffs. Black shoes and stockings, however, continued as a standard of dress. During the tenure of Fannie Forth as superintendent of nurses, 1932-1935, the uniform was changed to a blue and white striped dress. Although dress standards were liberalized, restrictions against smoking and drinking remained in effect. The *Student Guide* of 1938 made it clear the school looked with disfavor upon student smoking and forbid any young lady from smoking in her room, in uniform, or anywhere in the hospital. As for drinking, the rules were unequivocal: "Those who indulge in the use of intoxicating liquors will be removed." The guide also admonished student nurses not to sit in parked cars in front of the nurses' home and pointed out that "demonstrative farewells in the doorway were unbecoming."

Student nurses represented all religious faiths and reflected the general policy of the hospital. The Board of Trustees and the White Cross Guild were other examples of interfaith cooperation. During the 1930s Dr. Benson set up an advisory board of 100 business, political and civic leaders representing all faiths and points of view, who provided assistance and input in the day-to-day operation of the hospital. This representation of all

First black professional employed by Methodist Hospital was Spurling Clark, a pharmacist, who also taught pharmacology in the School of Nursing. He joined the hospital in 1937 after graduation from the Indianapolis College of Pharmacy, now the School of Pharmacy at Butler University. Mrs. Clark gave birth to the first black baby born at Methodist, Donald Thomas Clark, on August 21, 1940. Clark resigned from Methodist in 1949 to develop his own drug store at 27th Street and Northwestern Avenue. (Photo courtesy of Mrs. Spurling Clark)

faiths in the operation of Methodist moved one man to write the board expressing his gratitude that all religions were represented on the hospital's governing board. The man was Rabbi Morris M. Feuerlicht, Senior Rabbi since 1907 of the Indianapolis Hebrew Congregation, a member of the executive committee of Methodist Hospital.

From its very beginning, volunteers played an important role in the day to day operation of Methodist Hospital. Shown here in a photograph taken about 1939, is a workshop of the Mother's Guild. Note the profusion of flowered dresses, the old-fashioned sewing machines and large spools of thread. The group was a forerunner of the White Cross Guild organized in 1932.

Chapter Eight

Of War and Peace

> *No great advance has ever been in science, politics or religion without controversy.*
> —Lyman Beecher

As Germany's jackbooted Nazi Legions began their march across Europe in 1939, Indianapolis, in common with the nation, mobilized for defense and then for war. In 1940, a year before the Japanese attack on Pearl Harbor, Methodist Hospital was designated Evacuation Hospital No. 18 as part of the United States Emergency Defense Program. Hospital officials and staff worked closely with the Indianapolis Fire Department in setting up emergency plans in the event of serious fires or sabotage.

Doctors and nurses avidly read newspaper reports on the war. Both groups were aware that if America became involved, thousands of doctors and nurses would be needed. Some had already volunteered and were serving in army camps throughout the United States as the nation's first draftees—chosen by lot in the first peace time draft— and were undergoing basic training. The draft had already taken some hospital workers, presaging personnel shortages that would plague hospitals throughout the war. In the meantime, the Indiana State Medical Association was working closely with the United States Procurement and Assignment Agency which would control the destiny of nearly two thousand doctors in the state. It could decide who would be designated as indispensable to his community and stay in civilian life, and who would enter the Army, Navy or Air Force.

When Japanese bombers attacked Pearl Harbor on Sunday, December 7, 1941, Indianapolis was among the best prepared cities in the nation. As "Toolmaker to the Nation," the city's factories were running full blast turning out the munitions of war. Nine thousand new homes were being built to house the city's exploding population. Allison

Histopathology laboratory in 1940s. The technician is developing tissue slides for microscopic examination to determine whether or not an abnormal condition is present, information essential to the treatment of the patient.

Uniforms in the picture reflect areas of service rendered by registered nurses during WWII.

Division of General Motors made needed aircraft engines and at one point during the war employed 23,019 persons who worked three shifts, seven days a week. Hundreds of other plants turned out products for a war whose logistics were staggering.

From the beginning, Methodist Hospital foresaw problems, the most serious of which was manpower. Early on, many hospital workers left for more lucrative jobs in the city's factories. Others were drafted. Doctors and nurses were drawn into the armed services in increasing numbers. By 1944, according to the State Medical Association, 1,260 Indiana doctors were in service. There was, however, no resulting decrease in patients; in fact,

because of the city's exploding population, there were more patients than ever and fewer people to care for them. To ease the help shortages, Methodist Hospital turned to volunteer workers, Red Cross workers, nurses' aides, White Cross Guild members—in fact, anyone willing to work. The hospital opened the school classrooms for Red Cross volunteer nurses' aides, and several of these groups were trained by instructors of the school, who volunteered to work extra hours. These volunteer workers, along with White Cross Guild members, worked under the direction of graduate nurses and provided an important base for wartime hospital service. In 1942, in compliance with the government's call for more student nurses, 130 young ladies were enrolled to become the largest class in the hospital's history. Three new faculty members and a full time librarian were engaged to take care of the influx of the students who were identified by a green hair ribbon and a hot water bottle pin.

The need for orderlies was especially acute and at one time Miss Bertha Pullen, superintendent of nurses, reported there was only one orderly per floor. To fill the gap and in response to a plea from Reverend W.C. Hartinger, Methodist Hospital chaplain, 19 Indianapolis ministers volunteered to work as orderlies one day per week. The group underwent a 13-hour instruction course given by Mrs. Ethel Polsgrove and Dr. Alvin T. Stone and were assigned to floors where shortages were most acute. The ministers made beds, gave baths, hustled bedpans, wheeled patients into surgery and performed a myriad of other duties. Chairman of the group was the Reverend Almon J. Coble.

As part of an overall wartime plan, the White Cross Guild organized the Pink Lady Service in 1941—the name derived from the pink smocks the ladies wore when on duty. Three hundred women volunteered for Pink Lady service the following year. Each agreed to serve at least one day a month for the duration of the war. They were trained by nursing personnel to assist with patient care activities under the supervision of hospital nurses. Some of the ladies served as receptionists.

In 1944, for the first time the White Cross Guild, its membership now nearly 3,000, moved into a home of its own, the White Cross Service Center, on the hospital grounds facing Senate Avenue and to the rear of the surgical wing of the hospital. The 90 by 125 feet building, built of non-priority concrete blocks provided a pleasant workshop for the guild members and served as an auditorium and recreation room for the School of Nursing and hospital functions. In case of necessity, the structure could be quickly converted into an emergency ward of more than 100 beds. A unique feature of the Guild Center was a large stone fireplace whose individual stones from distant places were donated by the nearly 60 White Cross Guilds. Carved in stone above the fireplace was the guild motto: "The luxury of doing good surpasseth every other personal enjoyment." In the words of one writer, the fireplace "is thought of as the altar of the White Cross where the spiritual warmth and sociability of White Cross serve as eternal helpers in the noble

Opened in 1944, the White Cross Service Center provided a workshop for members as well as an auditorium and recreational center for the School of Nursing. In case of an emergency, the building could be converted to a 100-bed emergency ward. The building was torn down in 1981 to make way for the new West Building.

work of the service." (When the center was torn down in 1981 to make way for the new West Building, the motto and cross stones were moved to the new White Cross Center at 1500 Stadium Drive, which previously housed the Finance Division offices).

The White Cross Guild was also active in the sale of War Bonds and stamps as were other groups in the hospital. Bonds and stamps were on sale in the hospital lobby and the half-hour Sunday morning "Methodist Hospital Voice," broadcast over WIBC, urged the purchase of bonds and stamps. There were also lighter moments. Dances for servicemen were held regularly in the Methodist Nurses' Home, a Christmas dance in

1942 providing one of the many highlights.

Meanwhile, the hospital was dealing with a problem that was not only local, but national: the baby boom. At no one time in history had so many babies been born. At Methodist Hospital, on one 100-degree day in July of 1941, 15 babies were born in a 24 hour period to set a new record for births in a single day. The baby boom, of course, only added to the hospital's problems and in 1944, Dr. Benson announced he was being forced to close an entire floor of 33 beds because of manpower shortages. "We have tried desperately to bridge the gap in our manpower shortage with volunteer help," he reported to the Board of Trustees, "but despite splendid cooperation we

One of the features of the new White Cross Guild Service Building, opened in 1944, was a stone fireplace whose individual stones were donated by nearly 60 White Cross Guilds. Above the mantel was a tablet with the Guild motto, "The luxury of doing good surpasseth every other personal enjoyment." Shown above on the day of the

building's dedication are (left to right): Mrs. John G. Benson, White Cross Guild organizer; Mrs. Harry L. Foreman, Guild president; and Miss Thelma Hawthorne, secretary to the hospital superintendent, and the hospital's oldest employee.

have not been able to solve the problem."

As the manpower shortage worsened, Dr. Benson reported in June of 1944, "Even dietitians and other professional members of the staff have been washing dishes to assist in the manpower emergency." Especially needed, he reported, were maids, orderlies, laundry employees, and technicians to replace workers who had either been drafted or moved to better paying jobs in war industries. Regularly issued public appeals provided only a handful of workers.

The hospital, Dr. Benson reported, normally cared for an average of 500 patients daily, but this had increased to 600 forcing the hospital to change single rooms into double rooms and double rooms into rooms for three patients. The quality of patient care also suffered. "For proper care," Dr. Benson said, "three persons are required per patient. With the manpower shortage and despite volunteer help, two persons are doing the work of three." As for help, the labor turnover was 60%, Dr. Benson reported, adding: "It is almost impossible to get help."

On the brighter side, there were announcements of new equipment installed during the 1940s. Among them was an electroencephalograph or brain wave machine, installed in 1942, and used for diagnosing and locating brain tumors as well as in the study of epilepsy and other brain conditions or injuries. One of the first in the nation and the first in Indiana, a special room was set aside for the equipment's use by the hospital neurological staff first under the direction of Dr. E. Vernon Hahn and later under the direction of Dr. John G. Greist who learned the technology in military service. A premature birth station, the first in the city and state, was established in 1943 and maintained by Hoosier theater men, members of Variety Club Tent No. 10. According to a story in *The Indianapolis News* the estimated cost to equip and maintain the station for a year was $6,000. In 1949 an anonymous benefactor presented an $11,000 gift for the purchase of a new terminal sterilization machine which provided for the preparation and bottling of infant formulas under controlled conditions of rigid cleanliness followed by complete sterilization.

The war years brought an important announcement: that Methodist Hospital had become the first institution in Indiana to sign an agreement as a participating hospital in the Blue Cross Hospital

It's attributed to Dr. Jewett V. Reed as being the first doctor in Indiana to open the head for therapeutic purposes. However, it was the efforts of Dr. E. Vernon Hahn, pictured above, that laid the groundwork at Methodist Hospital in neurosurgery that has developed into the Neuroscience Center — the state's largest referral center for neurological diseases. It has the only unit in Indiana devoted to the treatment of acute spinal cord injuries.

Service, a mutual non-profit hospital insurance plan. Although Blue Cross is now a part of many families' insurance protection, its introduction in 1944 was big news and a revolutionary step in providing health care. Its rates in those long gone days also appear revolutionary. Membership fees were as low as 65 cents a month for a single membership to $2 a month for complete family protection.

Established under the sponsorship of the Indiana State Hospital Association, the original Blue Cross was headed by Sister Mary Reginald of Dyer. Guy W. Spring, formerly assistant director of the Blue Cross Hospital Service, Cincinnati, Ohio, served as executive director.

The drug store and soda fountain was a popular place for employees and doctors to take a break with a friend or to informally consult about a common concern while sipping a soda.

In announcing Methodist Hospital's participation in Blue Cross, Dr. Benson said the hospital had constantly "opposed the many so-called group hospitalization plans heretofore offered, for we felt none of them appeared to be sound or adequate and offered no relief that could be securely depended upon." In Blue Cross, however, the hospital found "a complete solution to the community problem of providing hospital care at a minimum cost to the individual. This plan pays the hospitals their necessary charges without exploitation or discrimination of other individual paying patients to help carry the cost of a group plan. Under this plan all hospitals, regardless of size or location, can participate without being compelled to suffer...deficits." Dr. Benson's statement also stressed that "The Blue Cross plan retains the privileges of democracy by allowing individual choice for hospital and physician. In no way does this plan involve medical practice..."

Dr. Benson also had another announcement to make in 1944. On March 15 of that year he announced his resignation as superintendent and general secretary, a post he had held for 13 years. The resignation did not come as a surprise since

The late 1930s and 40s saw a greater emphasis on medical education and strengthening of the role of the medical staff in the life of the hospital. A reorganization of the staff in 1945 recognized the developing trend toward specialties in the practice of medicine. Shown here is the Methodist Hospital Resident House Staff for 1939-40.

there had been rumors for months of an impending resignation as the result of growing tension between the superintendent and the newly organized medical staff who, it was said, were dissatisfied and displeased with Dr. Benson's tight administrative control. In Benson's defense, many of the controls may have been necessary in order to bring the hospital through a depression and most of a war.

Dr. Benson's letter of resignation, however, provided the basic reason for his retirement three years before reaching age 65. "A year ago," he told the board, "Mrs. Benson and I made up our minds that just as quickly as the (hospital) debt was removed, I would ask to be relieved...After $36,000 is paid sometime in June, the debt is gone."

Reviewing his years at the hospital, Dr. Benson said that when he took over a "desperate situation"

existed in that the hospital carried an enormous debt "and it looked as though it would be necessary to default the interest due on the mortgage, collateral notes, etc....Ninety percent of the job was the matter of debt."

In commenting on Dr. Benson's resignation, the Reverend Dr. Titus Lowe, Bishop of the Indiana Area and Chairman of the Board of Trustees, said, "Methodist Hospital owes an enormous debt for the long years of service he (Dr. Benson) has rendered the situation...It has been a rare privilege to be a member of this Board during all the time of Dr. Benson's service...I have been amazed, time and time again, at the vision he has had."

The Board voted to accept Dr. Benson's resignation but, acceding to Dr. Benson's wishes, voted that he continue as general secretary. Named to the

A buffet dinner and reception for upward of 150 physicians returning from military service in WWII was held March 20, 1946 in White Cross Service Center by Methodist Hospital and its medical staff. Over 214 of medical staff members were on hand to greet them. Shown here from

L. to R.: Dr. Robert E. Neff, Superintendent; Dr. William M. Dugan, president of medical staff, with returning physicians Frank P. Ramsey, Paul G. Iske, James T. Pebworth, and Glen V. Ryan.

post of acting superintendent was the Reverend Dr. Orien W. Fifer, a member of the Board of Trustees and former editor of *The Christian Advocate.* A former pastor of the Central Avenue Methodist Church, Dr. Fifer was also a past district superintendent of the Indianapolis District of the Methodist Church.

To select a new superintendent, the Board of Trustees named a committee of six. A statement by Dr. Guy O. Carpenter of the Board set the policy for the search. "In the appointment of Dr. Fifer as Acting Superintendent, I would not want the committee selecting a new superintendent to get the mistaken idea this is a place to draw a man from the pastorate. If necessary, I would like to move that the committee, in looking for a new superintendent, secure a man who has had hospital experience as an administrator of a hospital." The

motion, seconded by Jean S. Milner, was adopted and, in a very real sense, marked the end of one era and the beginning of another.

The search for a new superintendent took more than a year. On September 21, 1945 Bishop Lowe announced the appointment of Dr. Robert E. Neff, a nationally known hospital administrator and administrator of the University of Iowa hospitals since 1928. There was some political significance in the appointment. Although the medical staff was usually involved in discussions concerning hospital operations, the staff was apparently not consulted in making the appointment.

Neff's credentials were impressive. Born in Eaton, Indiana, the 58-year old administrator was a graduate of Indiana University and Iowa State College, where he earned his graduate degree. From 1911 to 1913 he was assistant to the bursar at

Methodist Hospital's lobby during the 1940s. Note the lounge area through the center arch. Dr. Clifford Hirshfield, one of the first interns in 1908, says that this was the sleeping quarters for interns when the hospital opened. It is now the location of the Mary Hanson Carey Memorial Chapel.

Testimonial for twenty years of service. Arthur V. Brown, president of Indiana National Bank, served as president of the Methodist Hospital Board of Trustees from 1922 to 1942 — the longest tenure of any president. The handsome scroll, above, was presented to him upon his retirement because of ill health.

Indiana University and later became head of the school's social service department. For several years he was administrator of the Indiana University Hospitals and superintendent of the Indianapolis City Dispensary from 1921 to 1928 before moving to his post at the University of Iowa. He was a former president of the Indiana Hospital Association; the Indianapolis Council of Social Agencies; the American Association of Social Workers, Indianapolis Chapter; Children's Hospital Associations of America; the University Hospital Executive Council and vice president of the Indiana State Health Council. A charter member of the American College of Hospital Administrators, he served as its president in 1935 and was president of the American Hospital Association in 1937.

Upon assuming his new duties Neff said: "The Indianapolis community deserves the best hospital service and the Methodist Hospital has an obligation to give the community the best there is in modern hospitalization. I fervently hope and pray that I may have the wisdom and the physical and spiritual strength to guide it on its way to provide this type of service."

And so began the tenure of the hospital's first professional administrator, marking the end of a period of many years in which Methodist ministers presided at the helm.

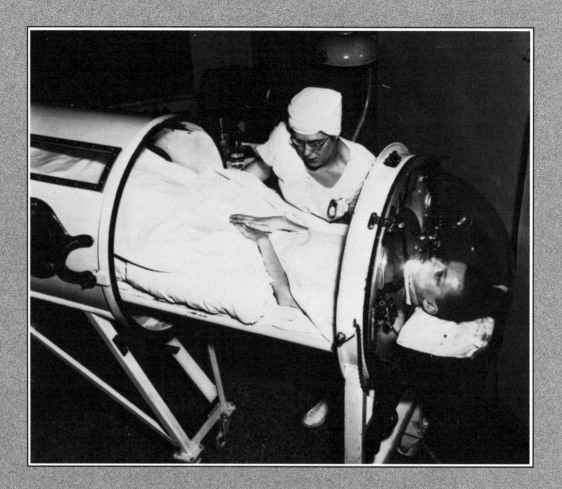

Chapter Nine

New Problems and An Anniversary

Methodist Hospital is a house of worship—not through ritual, robes and sermons, but through deeds of love and mercy.
— Bishop Richard C. Raines
Dedicatory Address
October 1956

A poliomyelitis (polio) patient encased in an iron lung at Methodist Hospital in the 1940s. The iron lung was a specially designed chamber to force normal breathing. Before the discovery of the Salk vaccine, polio epidemics were common during the summer months. A cruel disease, polio caused muscle atrophy, paralysis, and often death.

When World War II ended in August of 1945, Indianapolis became a city of cheering, shouting, joyous masses of people who packed the downtown streets and the Circle. Church bells, fire bells, factory whistles, sirens, automobile horns sounded, the noise reaching into the wards and offices and corridors of Methodist Hospital only blocks away. At the hospital, doctors and nurses made their rounds with smiles and a lighter step. At long last, it was over.

The year 1945 was also a banner year for the hospital. For the first time in its history, it was no longer in debt. The indebtedness of more than a million dollars, which had hung over the hospital like a dark, menacing shadow for most of its 46 years, was now paid off. There was little time, however, to celebrate. For the Board of Trustees the problem of the debt was already being replaced with a whole new set of problems, many of them growing out of the war and crucial to the continued operation of the hospital. In the meantime, there was a new superintendent and returning doctors, nurses and employees to be welcomed.

The new superintendent, Robert E. Neff, assumed his new duties on December 1, 1945 and to mark the occasion a reception was held at the hospital coincident with the dedication of a new $35,000 tunnel linking Methodist Hospital to the nurses' home and its four annexes. The program, which was held in the nurses home, included the cutting of a ribbon by Mr. Neff and Bishop Lowe. The tunnel, the construction of which had been long delayed because of the hospital's inability to acquire the necessary land, was 294 feet long and ran under 18th Street.

By the end of 1945 and well into 1946, Methodist Hospital was welcoming home its returning doc-

Robert E. Neff was Methodist Hospital's first professional hospital administrator. Appointed in 1945, he served until 1954 when he was succeeded by his assistant, Jack A.L. Hahn, also a professional administrator.

tors, nurses and staff employees who had served with honor in the nation's armed forces and home bases or on far-flung fronts in the European and Pacific Theaters of War. In all, 217 doctors and 170 nurses served with the armed forces and three lost their lives: Dr. John F. Kerr, Jr. and Nurses Ann Merrill and Betty Howren. Miss Howren, of New Castle, was killed in February, 1944 while helping evacuate soldiers in a flying ambulance from a battlefield in Sicily. Miss Merrill was killed in March of 1945 on a similar mission in India. The casualty lists also included Dr. Hawthorne Darby, among the first women to intern at Methodist Hospital. A medical missionary, she lost her life in the Philippines. Many persons on the hospital staff mourned the loss of sons, friends and relatives. Trustee O.J. Neighbours received word of his son's death prior to a Board meeting.

Most of the returning doctors, 150 of them, were welcomed home with a buffet dinner in March of 1946 at the White Cross Service Center. Besides swing music and a dinner with apple pie and cheese on the side, the returnees—their bronze discharge buttons glinting in their lapels—heard a group of speakers that included Bishop Lowe; superintendent Neff; the Reverend James W. Clarke of St. Louis, Missouri; Dr. Frank B. Ramsey, representing the veterans; Dr. William N. Wishard, Jr.; and Dr. William M. Dugan, president of the hospital medical staff.

In common with most public and private corporations, Methodist Hospital had been planning for the post-war years. On the desk of each member of the Board of Trustees was a copy of a 47-page planning document, "Horizons of Health" which had been compiled by a nine-man planning committee headed by the Reverend Dr. Guy O. Carpenter. The report was subtitled, "Yesterday's Dreams, Today's Realities, Tomorrow's Hopes." The report listed seven post-war projects: an addition to the nurses home, a new maternity building, a new lobby, a dietetic service building, a physicians' building, out-patient and psychiatry building and a unit for convalescents and "incurables" including the aged. Total cost of the projects the committee estimated between two and three million dollars.

The report also recommended a program of public health education, continued cooperation with the Blue Cross Hospitalization Plan, a retirement pension for employees, recognition of White Cross workers for their invaluable service, special training of young ministers by way of an internship, continued cooperation with the American College of Surgeons and maintenance of the Grade A classification, and appointment of a medical director. The planners also recommended that the superintendent of nurses continue to be in charge of the School of Nursing and that every effort be made to gain full approval and recognition by the National League of Nursing. The planners' recapitulation on page 46 of the report is worth reprinting:

1. A re-affirmation of the charity and volunteer nature of Christian hospitalization in cooperation with all faiths and in behalf of all who need it.

2. A strengthening of the administrative framework of the Methodist Hospital to

A 1940s nursing station.

enable it to carry its variety of healing aids for the sick.

3. A sound business program that will do all the free and part pay work possible and forever remain out of the toils of complicated long time indebtedness.

4. The full acceptance of the scientific and educational ideas of the medical and nursing profession pledging cooperation for the future needs.

5. A building program to meet future needs of the community approximating an expenditure of $2,000,000 to be accomplished by the year 1950 if possible.

6. A Public Health Education Program in cooperation with community agencies to reduce the casualties of unnecessary illness.

7. The building of a great institution of scientific healing upon a voluntary nonprofit basis giving to the public every advantage, resulting from the cooperation of religion, philanthropy and science in the modern battle against disease and for the developing of a greater physical fitness for all.

The plan was generally well received by the Board of Trustees and the new superintendent. Execution of the plan, however, would prove dif-

ficult. The hospital was faced with rising costs, overcrowding due to a serious shortage of beds and a critical shortage of nurses as well as a need to expand. The problem was city-wide and nationwide. The American Hospital Association was already sounding the tocsin. A United Press story reported that "the demand for hospitalization is running ahead of ability to supply enough nurses and beds, presenting a 'serious situation' in maintaining adequate hospital care."

There was talk in Indianapolis of possible hospital closings because of continued soaring costs and some administrators told *The Indianapolis Star*, "The vicious circle of increasing operating costs and resultant jumps in fees to patients may carry expenses of hospitalization beyond the reach of most citizens." Superintendent Neff told the newspapers that operating costs at Methodist had increased 111 percent since 1941 and that charges for drugs, cotton and surgical supplies were "still going up." Rates had also increased as the result of post-war inflation. Rates for private rooms jumped from $6, $7 and $8 in 1941 to $12, $13.50 and $15 in 1947. Ward charges increased from $3.50 to $6.50 and $7 and charges for a bed in a two-bed room, formerly $4 and $4.50, were set at $7.50 and $9.

Rising costs, however, were only part of the problem. The shortage of nurses was acute and the Board and Superintendent Neff mobilized to recruit nurses and student nurses. As an initial step, tuition at the Methodist Hospital School of Nursing was reduced from $75 to $50 a year without charge for textbooks. It was the second time the tuition fee had been cut; the year before it had been reduced from $150 to $75. On-the-job training courses for nurses' aides were renewed with Mrs. Helen Johnson as instructor assisted by Mrs. Ruth M. Bryan. Methodist ministers, alarmed that the hospital might find it necessary to close some of its 726 beds, joined in a recruiting program to encourage young girls to become nurses. The Reverend Dr. Claude M. McClure, appointed in 1947 as hospital chaplain, spurred the campaign by writing to 645 ministers asking them to find "young women of high scholastic ability and good character who will make first-class nurses." In addition to the letters, Dr. McClure mailed posters showing nurses at work; the posters to be prominently displayed in Sunday School rooms and high schools.

The early interns' and residents' educational program was primarily experience in caring for patients. By the 1940s they had a well-stocked library with medical texts and journals as part of a curriculum.

It remained, however, for an Indianapolis businessman, Edward F. Gallahue, president of the American States Insurance Company, to provide a practical solution. Gallahue first heard of the hospital's plight from Dr. Sumner L. Martin, Indianapolis District Superintendent, and Methodist Hospital Trustee, who told the insurance executive that after the June graduation the hospital would have only 100 students remaining of the 325 needed to properly operate the hospital. Gallahue, a Methodist layman, advised Dr. Martin, "What you need to do is handle this like we sell insurance." Dr. Martin invited Gallahue to try it.

Gallahue went to work. He got the cooperation of the bishop, 17 district superintendents and the 350,000 church members and their 750 ministers. Footing the cost himself, he visited all of the Methodist summer youth camps accompainied by Hugh Wriggelsworth, of the American States Insurance Company, and Dr. McClure. The Campers were shown a film which dramatized a career in nursing and the challenges and rewards nursing of-

fered. After the film and a short talk, cards were distributed and girls were asked to indicate their interest. Using the cards as an insurance salesman would a prospect file, ministers paid calls on interested young ladies. Follow-up mailings extolling a career in nursing went out regularly. And with the blessing of Bishop Richard C. Raines, meetings were organized in all of the church's 17 districts with each minister and president of the Women's Society for Christian Service assigned to recruit at least one student nurse.

In 1949 one of the largest beginning classes in recent Methodist history was enrolled and the "Gallahue Plan" listed 1,118 other Methodist young ladies interested in becoming nurses. "The secret," Gallahue said, "was a well organized year-round recruitment program. A nurse recruitment program is not a shot-in-the-arm promotion once or twice a year, but a year-round plan properly organized...that will reach into every nook and corner of the state."

Although there was some criticism of the so-called "Gallahue Plan", it became known as the "Indiana Plan" and gained national attention when it became the subject of an article in the *Reader's Digest.*

Shown here is Dr. Harold C. Ochsner, head of the radiology department, conducting a seminar for interns and residents around 1949 — before the days of air conditioning — note the open window for ventila-
tion. The first formal teaching of medicine at Methodist Hospital was a course in X-ray diagnosis by Dr. Raymond C. Beeler. It was sponsored by the Medical Research Society, progenitor of today's medical staff.

Help in recruiting nurses came from other sources including the White Cross Guild which established three $300 cash scholarships for the Methodist Hospital School of Nursing. Other contributions came in from civic and women's groups. The American Legion made contributions through the efforts of Dr. Lester Bibler. The Indianapolis Junior Chamber of Commerce launched "Nurse Enrollment Week." Local newspapers cooperated with publicity and editorials and *The Indianapolis Star* ran a series discussing why many young women decided against a nursing career—a series which resulted in several reforms including improved salaries for graduate nurses.

Methodist Hospital also took yet another well publicized step to make nursing more attractive to young ladies—it relaxed many of the nursing school's rigid rules and put new emphasis on social and recreational opportunities. Among the new in-

novations were tennis, horseshoes, shuffleboard and badminton courts, all installed at a cost of $3,500. Superintendent Neff also announced the appointment of a librarian and a full-time social director, Miss Mildred Sweet, a deaconess. Students, he said, would be urged to participate in a variety of activities that included athletics, choral club, Christian fellowship program, bridge and dancing clubs. The hospital also provided nurses and students with membership in the Riviera Swim Club and regularly distributed tickets to symphony concerts.

The nursing shortage, however, was not the only problem of postwar Indianapolis hospitals. All city hospitals remained overcrowded and, in some cases, patients were required to wait as long as 60 days before being admitted. Superintendent Neff reported that at Methodist advance notice of three to five weeks was required, the only exception being acute medical cases. The hospital was also sending new mothers and their babies home earlier. Where formerly a mother and baby remained in the hospital for nine or ten days, they were now being sent home after five days, providing, of course, there were no complications. A new technique of getting surgical patients on their feet more quickly was employed with the view of shortening their hospital stay. To further alleviate overcrowding, an extensive out-patient service was inaugurated.

An admission plan, adopted in 1947, restricted a physician's reservations to two patients per day instead of the former practice of admitting three. The change was made to spread the hospital service over a larger number of physicians. The plan of scheduling operations was also changed to permit improved coordination with patient reservations. Despite the new policy, the hospital continued to

face a demand for patient service in excess of available facilities and in 1948 was carrying a reservation list of elective cases extending about 35 to 40 days in advance. In addition, Superintendent Neff reported, the hospital was coping with 25 or 30 emergency cases daily. It was also a firm rule that all patients must be referred by a physician and, under no circumstances, was a patient to be referred by the hospital administration.

The acute shortage of Indianapolis hospital facilities was underscored by a petition signed by some 50 local doctors and presented to the Medical Council of the Indianapolis Medical Society. The doctors warned that unless something was done, Indianapolis faced "an actual deterioration in standards of medical care." In its coverage of the story *The Indianapolis Star* reported, "the physicians declared that all of the city's hospitals are overcrowded 'to the bursting point' and that some

Bishop Titus Lowe, president of the Methodist Hospital Board of Trustees, cuts the ribbon marking the opening of the tunnel connecting the hospital to Wile Hall. Standing at his right is Hospital Superintendent Robert Neff. The date is December 1, 1945.

would-be patients are required to wait as long as 60 days before gaining admission to a hospital, and that sufficient beds are not always available to take care of emergency cases, such as automobile accident victims who require immediate hospitalization."

A group of one-hundred physicians on the staff at Methodist Hospital was also in the news. Angered by a hospital memorandum that warned of possible dismissal if the doctors failed to attend staff meetings, the doctors charged Methodist officials with "regimentation" and alleged they were "being treated like a bunch of grade school children." The news stories, which seemed to favor the doctors' side of the controversy, also provided an insight into the problem of overworked doctors in a day of overcrowded hospitals and an increased patient load. The shortage of beds, the doctors pointed out, made it impossible for a physician to have all his patients in one hospital and part of his day involved traveling from one hospital to another. In addition, there were regular office hours and visits to homebound sick patients—all necessary and time consuming and leaving little or no time for attending meetings. A number of young physicians, recently returned from military service, were quoted as saying they would be hard pressed "to make a go of it" if the Methodist attendance requirement was enforced.

In the middle of the controversy was Robert E. Neff, Superintendent, who had written but not signed the offending memorandum. Neff told the Board of Trustees that staff attendance was required by the American College of Surgeons for accrediting purposes—a requirement that presented a problem in a hospital with more than 600 physicians on its staff. At Methodist, the executive committee of the medical staff had set a minimum requirement of attendance at eight meetings out of a total of 24 meetings annually. "Some members of the staff feel that even that requirement is out of order," Neff reported, "and object particularly to the element of compulsion as included in the American College of Surgeons program of minimum standards." Citing the importance of the College's approval, Neff said, "The modern hospital today would have a difficult time explaining to its clientele and its community the reasons for lack of approval by the American College of Surgeons."

In a sense the controversy reflected the problems of the 1940s and the 1950s and the conditions under which hospital administrators, staff employees, nurses and doctors labored. Everyone was overworked and under the worst possible conditions. Neff, according to those who remembered him, was a good administrator who ran a "tight ship." His job, however, was no sinecure. With one hand he had to administer a large overcrowded hospital complex under trying conditions and insure that patients and doctors were treated fairly in regard to admission and treatment. Methodist had always been proud of its national reputation for excellence and Neff was determined to maintain the hospital's standards despite the fact that even the very halls had been pressed into service to provide extra patient beds. On the other hand, he had to assuage the doctors keeping in mind their practice was dependent upon the accessibility of hospital facilities while keeping hundreds of employees, including nurses, working and happy.

To complicate matters the Board of Trustees, in common with other hospitals in the community, was reluctant to risk any new construction programs. Most remembered the overbuilding of the earlier years when hospital beds had lain idle and whole wings were closed. Others were reluctant to assume a new indebtedness. This was particularly true at Methodist, which had only just paid off an onerous debt that had hung over the hospital down through the years and even threatened to close its doors during the Great Depression.

To offset the lack of new construction, Methodist launched a program of renovation and remodeling designed to provide additional beds in already existing space and to repair and renovate those areas of the hospital which had been neglected because of war time strictures and a lack of help. The 5-North Ward was remodeled at a cost of $47,153 to provide 23 beds where there had formerly been 10. A fifth floor connection between B Building and 5 Center was established so that a new modern elevator of the push button type could be installed. Corridors were repainted and new light fixtures installed in the corridors of "A" Building. Other improvements included installation of new refrigeration equipment, modernization of the nurses' cafeteria, and a new health service for student nurses installed in Wile Hall. All of these improvements cost money and posed yet another problem for hard pressed hospital administrators. Prices were high; it was a seller's

Dr. Willis D. Gatch, dean of Indiana University School of Medicine, 1932-1946, maintained a large private practice of surgery. Noted for his devotion to the principles and practice of surgery, he maintained an abiding interest in his students and methods of teaching. While a surgery resident at Johns Hopkins, he invented the Gatch bed, fore-runner of modern adjustable hospital beds. Methodist Hospital's Board of Trustees made a special recognition of his contribution to graduate medical education in the early 1950s. Shown here, he is being recognized at a dinner by the interns and residents for his role in their education.

market, and much needed equipment was still in short supply. Superintendent Neff grumbled openly about the "independent attitude" of the hospital's suppliers.

The demand for hospital care, however, continued unabated and, in fact, was becoming more and more serious with each passing day. Statistics for the ten-year period from 1938 through 1947 tell the story of a hospital attempting to care for almost twice as many patients in the same amount of space. In 1938 Methodist admitted 14,853 patients, but in 1947 admissions totaled 22,739. Births in 1938 numbered 1,595, but by 1947 the hospital was recording 4,788—all part of the war and post-war baby boom. Patient days also increased dramatically, from 154,393 in 1938 to 224,311 in 1947. And, in the same ten year period, daily occupancy rates rose from 423 to 615.

The shortage of beds in Indianapolis engendered much discussion and some planning. Over in Irvington, the North Irvington Civic League discussed the possibility of erecting a $2,500,000 east side hospital. At Methodist, Bishop Titus Lowe appointed a committee to consider the construction of new buildings and facilities for psychiatric and tuberculosis treatment as well as expanded maternity wards. Although federal money was available for construction, such gifts from Washington were viewed with suspicion, particularly by doctors and good Republicans, who feared it was another attempt by the government to "socialize" the hospital and medical industries. The South Indiana Conference of the Methodist Church, under leadership of Bishop Richard C. Raines—successor to Bishop Lowe—was among the first to vote against accepting federal funds under the new Hill-Burton Act that provided money for hospital construction. The bed shortage which would continue to grow, would not be solved until the 1950s when an aroused community would take action.

Despite bed shortages, inflation and the multiplicity of post-war problems, Methodist Hospital remained committed to excellence. Neff appeared before the hospital's professional and lay staffs to emphasize that commitment and to stress the value of "little things" that made a patient's hospital stay easier. In one talk, he described these "little things" as "those comparatively smaller services and niceties beyond what a patient expects and which we can render as extra service if we have that generous, kind, sympathetic spirit, and the heartfelt desire to please our patients and clientele."

Modernization and rehabilitation of hospital facilities continued unabated in lieu of a building program. Wile Hall was completely refurbished. New equipment was purchased and installed in patient rooms and a new Infant Formula Laboratory, said to be one of the most modern in the United States, was completed. A sump pump was installed in the main ambulance entrance to offset flooding during heavy rains. Additional fire and explosion preventive measures were installed and the hospital's sprinkler system was expanded and improved. Superintendent Neff personally inspected or supervised the changes, roaming the hospital corridors and rooms at all hours, his grey hair and prominent hearing aid a familiar sight throughout the hospital. As an economy measure designed to eliminate contractors and expensive bidding, Neff added several craftsmen to the hospital staff, including plumbers, steamfitters, carpenters and painters.

Coping with the excessive demands being made upon a hospital with a critical shortage of beds was an embarrassment for both the hospital and physicians. Reporting on the problem in 1950, Superintendent Neff told the Board of Trustees; "The pressure has become so strong and the competition so keen for the limited available beds that doctors or their authorized representatives line up at the reservations office as long as four hours in advance of the 2 p.m. opening of the reservation list for 'urgent cases.' This situation we regret very much. It is undignified and presents a spectacle that is frequently embarrassing. For example, one of our well known surgeons sat in the reservations office a few days ago and read a book for three hours awaiting his turn to make an urgent reservation...As many as twenty emergency cases presented by physicians have been held off at the close of almost every day during the past several weeks."

Younger doctors, who had not served in World War II, faced yet another problem: they were still subject to military duty. Although the war was over, America continued to draft young men with a resulting need for doctors in U.S. camps and bases as well as overseas. As for deferments, the Medical Council passed a resolution stating that "under the circumstances prevailing at present, the hospital cannot request deferment for any doctor properly qualified for service...on the grounds that he is essential for the operation of the hospital." To boost morale and allay apprehensions that a doctor called up for military service might lose his hospital privileges, the Board of Trustees, on the recommendation of the Medical Council, established a policy that provided reappointment each year and immediate promotion in his staff standing upon his honorable discharge and return.

Surgeons at Methodist Hospital helped write medical history in 1947 and 1948 by performing unique operations that saved the lives of three babies. The 1947 operation involved the correction of an unusual malformation connecting a newborn Indianapolis boy's stomach with his windpipe instead of his mouth. The baby's esophagus, the tube that leads from the mouth to the stomach, was separated into two parts, the upper portion coming to a dead end, while the lower part was connected to the windpipe where it separated into two sections leading into the lungs.

The 1948 operations, believed to be medical firsts, involved the lives of a tiny Tipton baby girl and a baby boy from Indianapolis. Both babies were born with total closure of the small intestines due to obstructions. The operations involved the removal of about one-third of the intestine and stitching the normal ends together, an operation complicated by the fact that the small intestine in a baby is only about one-eighth of an inch in diameter. The Indianapolis baby posed a special problem in that he had been born at least a month prematurely and was but four days old when he was taken to the operating room. An improvised incubator of hot water bottles was banked about him during the surgery. Surgeons in neither of the cases were identified; medical ethics of the 1940s banned such publicity.

Methodist Hospital continued to make news in other areas. The hospital's long time liberal policy toward women was again underscored in 1948 when two women, Dr. Ada R. Perel of Whiting and Dr. Gwendelyne Peck of Oklahoma City, were among sixteen interns entering Methodist on July 1.

The late forties also brought other changes. William G. Schiltges, president of the Fletcher Trust Company, was named president of the Methodist Hospital Board of Trustees in 1948. Dr. Roy A. Geider became the new president of the medical staff in 1947 succeeding Dr. William M. Dugan. Dr. Charles F. Thompson was named president-elect for 1948. There was also a new superintendent of the school of nursing and nursing service, Miss E. Louise Grant of Minneapolis, Minnesota. Miss Grant succeeded Miss Hazel Whittern. Dr. Ralph O. Pearson, pastor of the Irvington Methodist Church, was named associate chaplain to work with Dr. McClure. (This was to allow Dr. McClure more time to work with churches across the state.) The new president of the White Cross Guild was Mrs. Arthur A.

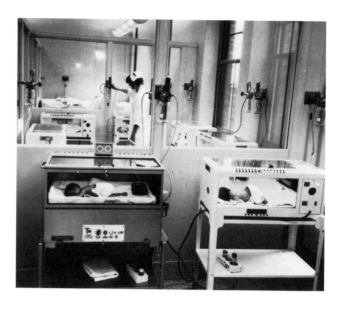

Providing obstetrical services was a critical problem for Methodist Hospital in the early 1950s — the birth rate had passed the 6000 a year mark. Shown here is the premature nursery which was also expanding rapidly. A new policy in 1951 limiting the hospital stay of new mothers to three days was an attempt to reduce pressure on the obstetrical department brought on by the "Baby Boom."

Fairbanks, a post to which she would be reelected in 1949. Twenty men and women employees received gold watches and pins, marking 20 years or more of service, at Methodist Hospital's first annual tenure party. Oldest employee in point of service was Mrs. Laura Horn of Indianapolis who joined the hospital in 1917.

In the closing months of 1949, Methodist Hospital marked the 50th anniversary of its 1899 incorporation with a six-day Golden Anniversary Celebration that began on October 28 with a nurses' homecoming and was climaxed by an anniversary dinner at the Murat Temple on November 2. Besides the gala homecoming program, the nurses staged an elaborate pageant, "Fifty Years of the Nursing Profession," at the White Cross Guild Center. The hospital's history was dramatized in a special radio show, "Down Through the Years," which was aired by WIRE from the auditorium of the Claypool Hotel. An open house was held the following day with members of the White Cross Guild acting as hostesses.

The Methodist Medical Staff, at a special meeting, looked back over its long history with papers presented by Dr. William N. Wishard, Dr. John A. MacDonald and Dr. Lester M. Hoyt, who presented a paper on the pioneer work of his men-

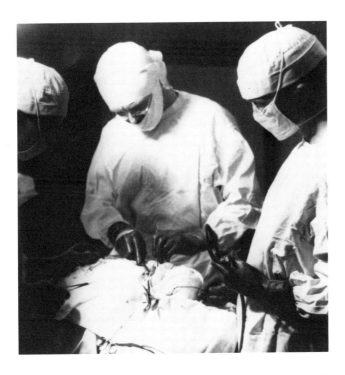

One of the pioneering doctors on Methodist Hospital's medical staff who helped pave the way for sub-specialties in medicine was Dr. Harold M. Trusler shown here in 1933 performing a surgical procedure on a person with a harelip, a congenital deformity in which the upper lip is split like that of a hare. In 1937 he became the first director of the Plastic Surgery Division at Indiana University School of Medicine. (Photo courtesy of Dr. H. Marshall Trusler)

tor and associate chief pathologist, Dr. Horace M. Banks. The staff took special note of the many advances in medicine particularly in the areas of the treatment of diabetes and pneumonia and the pioneering work of members of the Methodist Medical Staff. A special guest at the program was Dr. Oliver C. Neier, now 84 years old, who had delivered the first baby in Methodist Hospital.

More than 800 persons from all walks of life attended the Golden Anniversary in the Murat Temple Egyptian Room and heard Congressman Walter H. Judd (R. Minn.) speak on "Christian Institutions in this Time of Transition." William B. Schiltges, president of the Board of Trustees, presided.

It was a glittering affair. The chorus of the school of nursing provided music and the Reverend Dr. McClure, hospital chaplain, presented a brief history of the hospital. Superintendent Neff introduced the speakers, Bishop Richard C. Raines introduced Con-

gressman Judd and the invocation and benediction were given by the Reverend Dr. Jean Milner and the Reverend Dr. Sumner L. Martin, both members of the Board of Trustees.

The 50 year-old hospital had much to be proud of and the dinner program included a litany of its many accomplishments. During its first 50 years the hospital had served 697,367 patients; trained 2,014 nurses; and provided experience and training for 518 interns and residents. A total of 50,330 babies entered the world within its walls.

"Today," the report continued, "the hospital, one of the largest of its kind in the world, has 624 beds and 86 bassinets. There are 331 physicians and surgeons on its active staff, 293 on the associate and courtesy staff. There are now 26 resident physicians and 20 interns with 197 regular graduate nurses and 278 nurses in training...The White Cross Guild, a great organization of women, with 2,700 members, is the outstanding Woman's Auxiliary in the United States."

It was, indeed, a proud record for a hospital only 50 years old and founded with only $4,750 in its treasury. Open to every class and creed, it was a monument to its high commitment to Christ and the philanthropy of thousands of people, both rich and poor. But perhaps a sentence in the Golden Anniversary program said it best: "The Methodist Hospital...is a striking example of a community hospital made possible by a benevolent people."

Among those who sat and listened to the speakers in the Murat Temple that night, there must have been many whose minds wandered from the glorious past to the realism of the present and the demands of the future. It was good to reflect on the hospital's growth and progress—those wonderful years that had brought big changes in hospital care and even greater changes in medicine—but what about the future that presaged even greater and more innovative changes? There could be no future, one reasoned, unless the problems of 1949 which were going to be carried over into the 1950s were solved: problems such as overcrowding, shortages, inflation, rising costs and the continuing need for both additional beds and funding. Could these problems be solved, put to rest, so that the largest hospital in Indiana and one of the largest in the world, could move on to new and better ways to serve its community and uphold its great traditions? It was a vital question for the new decade.

Chapter Ten

Old Problems, New Solutions

> *All streams run to the sea, but the sea is not full; To the place where the streams flow, There they flow again.*
> —Ecclesiastes 1:7

As Methodist Hospital entered the 1950s all the problems of the preceding decade —excessive demands for services and shortages of beds, nurses, doctors and hospital personnel—continued to plague the hospital's administration. The problems not only persisted, but insisted on growing. Superintendent Neff's reports to the Board of Trustees continued to present a portrait of dedicated people coping daily with an endless series of crises.

By 1953 the waiting list for elective patients was 75 days. As for emergency cases, Neff reported, "the demands cannot be met from day to day, even though we admit 35 or 40 patients." There was a note of resignation in his year end report. "We wonder," he wrote, "just how much further services can be expanded in view of our present physical limitations."

One of the hospital's most critical problems was providing obstetrical services. The birth rate, which had passed the 6,000 a year mark and showed no immediate signs of diminishing, was straining the department to the breaking point. In 1951 new regulations went into effect that limited obstetric admissions to 92 patients, reduced stays to three days, and provided that no patient was to be admitted unless it had been previously determined that a bed was available. Patients were to be admitted on a "first come, first serve" basis.

Despite the critical demands on the hospital, it was a continuing policy that no one was to be turned away because of inability to pay. The matter of the patient's ability to pay was not to be discussed until the patient had been admitted and treatment was underway. The policy was liberal, humane, and costly. Where once the annual cost of treating charity or "guest" patients had been around

The new psychiatric wing, opened in 1959, had all the comforts and little amenities of living at home. Dr. David A. Boyd, secretary of the American Board of Psychiatry said, "By bringing psychiatric care into the general hospital setting, Methodist Hospital is leading a national trend...the patient enters the hospital voluntarily and becomes a party to his treatment. The team is important. Mental illness is not a thing apart from the whole body of medicine."

$75,000, these costs passed the $90,000 mark in the mid-fifties.

For the first time, in the 1950s, Methodist Hospital took advantage of federal funds to carry out innovations. The Board of Trustees approved the use of such funds, available under the Hospital Survey and Construction Act, after Superintendent Neff assured the board there were "no strings attached" and acceptance did not include governmental control of the hospital in any way. The first grant was for $147,000, a second for $300,000. Among the changes carried out was an addition to the 5 North Ward where 15 new beds were installed and a passageway built between the B and A Buildings.

The shortage of personnel continued to be a real problem. The number of interns and residents was increased to meet approval requirements of the American Medical Asociation, but the problem of hiring more graduate nurses was more serious. The nursing shortage was so critical that often the hospital could not meet the demands of the surgical staff for operating room assistance and surgical patients were often subject to long waits and delays. Particularly difficult, was finding nurses for the evening and night shifts. Nurses were in a seller's market and could virtually dictate the hours they would work. Adding to the problem was the new 40-hour work week for nurses. Now a federal law, the shorter work week made it necessary. to hire still more nurses. To attract nurses, Miss Fredericka Koch, the new superintendent of nurses and director of the school of nursing who had succeeded Miss Grant, joined with hospital authorities in an extensive advertising and recruiting program. The shortage of orderlies and other non-professional help was also critical. The Korean War, which had begun in June of 1950, and a highly competitive market made hiring difficult.

Adding to the pressures were a series of polio epidemics, the first in 1949 and the second in 1951. In the latter year, 78 cases were admitted to Methodist. There was, however, assistance from the National Foundation for Infantile Paralysis and the local Red Cross helped with equipment and personnel. The Foundation provided additional iron lungs and hot pack treatments. Happily, it was also among the last stands of the dreaded disease which over the years had taken thousands of lives and left other thousands paralyzed. In 1954 Dr. Jonas Salk would develop an anti-polio serum

One of the few private rooms available to patients in 1950's.

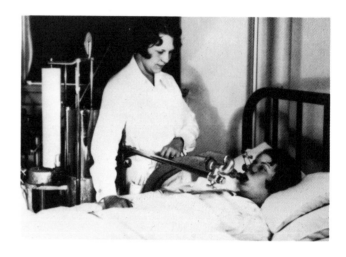

Above, a member of the respiratory therapy department is conducting pulmonary function tests on a patient.

and innoculate the first school children in Pittsburg, Pa. Two years later, Dr. Albert Sabin would introduce an oral vaccine.

Throughout this trying period the hospital managed to remain in the black and on a firm financial base without incurring any new indebtedness. There were, however, increases in patient costs to offset rising costs of equipment, supplies and personnel. A comparative study showed that in 1939 the average stay at Methodist Hospital was 12 days with an average charge of $11.35 per day and a total average bill of $136.20; in 1951 the average stay was eight days with an average daily charge of $17.40 and a total average cost of $139.60. The shorter hospital stay in 1951, four days less than in 1939, reflected the hospital's policy of getting patients on their feet sooner and

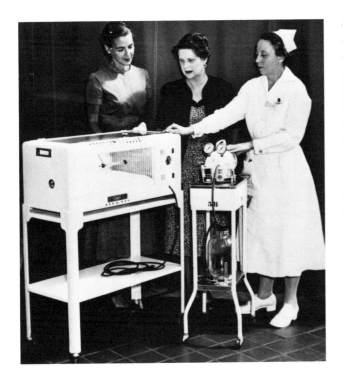

Much needed equipment in 1955 came from many sources. Mrs. Everett Potter and Mrs. Marie Gilson, president of the White Cross Children's Cheer Guild, present an incubator and aspirator to Miss LaVonne Mundy, supervisor of the Taggart Memorial Children's Unit, who graciously accepts the equipment.

sending them home as soon as possible.

It was also a time of new medical developments and new discoveries. The tranquilizer, Miltown, came into general use and antihistamines became a popular remedy for colds and allergies. Isotopes came into use in medicine, the first contraceptive pill of phosphorated hesperidin was produced, lasers were developed and in 1955 Dorothy Hodgkin discovered Vitamin B-12. The still new drugs, penicillin and streptomycin, were proving effective and in 1951, more than 400,000 pounds of penicillin and 350,000 pounds of steptomycin were produced.

In the 1950s the surgeon general of the U.S. confirmed what many doctors already knew: that lung cancer was directly linked to cigarette smoking. The findings were followed, in 1960, by a report from the American Heart Association that a higher death rate among middle aged men was caused by heavy cigarette smoking. Methodist Hospital, which had always frowned upon smoking, obtained a research grant in 1965 to develop a smoking withdrawal program for patients. Directed by the Medical Research Department, the program was

administered by the Reverend Dr. Kenneth E. Reed and Chaplain Edgar E. Filbey. Later, in the 1970s on the recommendation of the medical staff, all cigarette vending machines were removed from the hospital and the sale of cigarettes and tobacco banned in hospital shops. Although the hospital could not prevent patients or visitors from smoking, such activities were limited to lounges. These rules remain in effect to this day.

The increasingly critical bed shortage at Methodist and other city hospitals drew the fire of civic-minded citizens and doctors and hardly a week passed that a local newspaper failed to carry a story on continuing hospital bed shortages, long waiting lists, and the need for more hospital beds. The hospitals, busy coping with daily crises, continued to resist incurring any new indebtedness or running the risk of overbuilding. They also remained opposed to accepting federal funds through fear of governmental control and "socialization" of hospitals.

An aroused Indianapolis citizenry finally produced action. Alarmed by the growing shortages of hospital beds in a growing city, they appeared before civic boards, made speeches, and circulated petitions which were signed by more than 9,000 Marion County property owners. The speeches, the petitions, the newspaper stories, and the pressures culminated in the organization of the Indianapolis Hospital Development Association (IHDA). Organized by a group of civic, medical, business and industrial leaders, the IHDA was incorporated on October 25, 1950 with the objective of raising funds to build new hospitals and providing for the expansion of existing hospitals. The officers of the IHDA were Edward F. Gallahue, president; Dr. J. William Wright, Sr., vice president; William H. Book, secretary; and William B. Schiltges, treasurer. Gallahue and Schiltges were members of Methodist Hospital's Board of Trustees.

In 1953, the IHDA launched a city wide campaign to raise $12,000,000 in voluntary contributions. The campaign, enthusiastically supported by the Indianapolis community, proved to be a success and $3,280,000 was allotted to Methodist Hospital for an expansion program. Plans went forward immediately for the construction of a nine-story 208-bed general hospital facility, expansion of the center wing which would house the professional services and, added later, a new "C" building to provide psychiatric services and expand educational facilities

As this major expansion program was getting underway, there was a new change in top management. Superintendent Neff, who had reached retirement age, announced his retirement, effective December 31, 1954. Methodist's first professional hospital administrator, Neff had served the hospital well for nine years which had included World War II, the Korean War years and the critical post-war years. These had been trying years and Neff obviously was tired and looking forward to a life free of the constant pressures of a hospital's daily and complex problems.

Neff was succeeded by a man who would leave an indelible imprint upon Methodist Hospital—Jack Albert Louis Hahn, who for the preceding two years had served as the hospital's assistant superintendent. A professional hospital administrator, Hahn was a graduate of the University of Evansville where he received his bachelor's degree in business administration. Following graduation from college, he served as a submarine officer in the U.S. Navy. He then took his master's degree in hospital administration at Northwestern University in 1948 and became assistant administrator of Memorial Hospital, Freemont, Ohio, a post he held for five years before accepting the assistant superintendency at Methodist. Hahn was the third in his family to become a top hospital administrator. His father, Albert G. Hahn, despite being blind, had been for many years administrator of the Deaconess Hospital at Evansville. He was secretary of the American Protestant Hospital Association for many years and is credited with being the most significant person in the development of the Protestant professional hospital chaplaincy. Jack Hahn's mother, Grace, was an assistant administrator at Deaconess Hospital.

The new superintendent, who assumed his duties on January 1, 1955, was a "take charge" type of administrator and committed to excellence. As Hahn confided later in an interview, he was satisfied that the hospital offered quality care, but it was only "adequate" and he wanted to lift its standards by strengthening its medical education program—a decision that found both strong support and opposition, generally because of its cost. A management consulting firm added fuel to the controversy: it said the hospital couldn't afford such a program and recommended Methodist

become just another community hospital. Hahn persisted, however, and brought in Dr. Mearle Backastow as the first full-time director of medical education. Earlier Dr. Warren E. Coggeshall had served as a part-time director and demonstrated the potential of a quality graduate medical education program. Dr. Backastow developed extensive plans but resigned before the program could be implemented. He was succeeded by Dr. Jack H. Hall on July 1, 1960. By the mid-1960s the program, which had been running in the red and was upsetting some of the Board members, was a viable one although cost continued to be a major concern. Hahn would later say, "Dr. Hall cannot be given enough credit for the program's success."

The 1950s brought an important change in the policy of all Indianapolis hospitals on the admission of blacks and other minorities who, up to this time, could only gain admission to City Hospital (now Wishard) unless they were from outside Marion County. The admission change was dictated by the Indianapolis Hospital Development Association which made integration a requirement for financing a hospital's expansion. Officials of IHDA took the position that money for the hospitals was being solicited from people in all walks of life and all races and creeds, and it was unfair to ask for solicitations from those who would be refused admission to the very hospital they were supporting. The participating hospitals promptly agreed to the proviso and for the first time all Indianapolis hospitals were open to blacks.

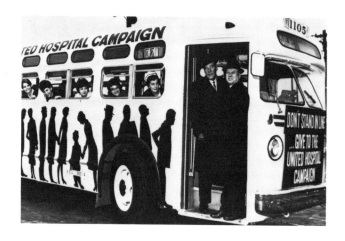

Even public transportation was enlisted to publicize the Indianapolis Hospital Development Association's drive for funds to build new hospital facilities and provide for the expansion of existing hospitals. The IHDA's first fund drive was launched in 1950.

Jack A. L. Hahn, superintendent of Methodist Hospital, 1955-1981. A nationally known hospital administrator, Hahn served longer than any other superintendent and left an indelible imprint on the hospital. Among the many national honors that came to him was the prestigious Distinguished Service Award of the American Hospital Association of which he was a former president.

Chester Warman, United Hospital Campaign Chairman for Methodist Hospital and Anderson Casion, one of Methodist's first employees, show pledge cards of 1965 and 1907. Mr. Casion worked as head porter and orderly for 25 years. Highly respected by physicians and staff, he resigned and went back to school and completed a course of study in podiatry, becoming a successful foot doctor. Through the years, he maintained a record of the financial contribution he made to Methodist Hospital in 1907.

When ill in body and hospitalized, it's easy for the mind and spirit to become depressed also. The patient library prepares books and magazines which are taken by Pink Ladies by cart to patients' rooms as part of the hospital's effort to care for the whole person.

It was a major triumph for the city's black community in a city which had always been highly segregated and which only a few decades before had been a citadel for the Ku Klux Klan.

Methodist Hospital had long been in the vanguard of those urging better treatment of blacks, but while its heart was in the right place, its words were not always supported by affirmative action. The crux of the problem lay in the reasoning that white patients would resent being hospitalized in the same ward or room with blacks. A suggestion that black interns be admitted was voted down on the grounds that the hospital's white patients would resent being treated by Negro doctors and lead to incidents. The hospital, however, was moving toward initial integration of its professional staff. In 1956 Sue Ann Perkins Winburn became the first black graduate of the Methodist School of Nursing and in the next ten years every graduating class included at least one black young lady.

Integration of the medical staff also moved slowly. Although the Medical Staff Council established a policy in 1948 of opening staff membership to all qualified physicians regardless of race, color or creed, it was not until March 25, 1954 that the Hospital elected the first black physicians to its staff: Dr. Harvey Middleton, Dr. E. Paul Thomas and Dr. Frank P. Lloyd.

Dr. Lloyd, who would have a long time impact on Methodist Hospital, was the son of an Episcopal priest, a native of Charleston, S.C., and a graduate of Howard University. Following his internship at Freedman's Hospital, Washington, D.C., the young obstetrician and gynecologist was named a Rockefeller Fellow at Columbia Presbyterian Medical Center, New York, a world famous center for the study of obstetrics. Later, he became a teacher at Columbia University. Dr. Lloyd came to Indianapolis in 1952, attracted by the city's "open door" policy toward black physicians. He was elected to the staff at Wishard Hospital and

One of Methodist Hospital's two interns when the hospital opened in 1908, Dr. Clifford Hirshfield (left) of Oklahoma City in medical library with Drs. William B. Hall, intern (center) and John B. Graham, resident, sharing lively tales of the early days. "There was no educational program in those days," he said. "Internship was purely a matter of service — nothing like this," he said as he looked at the well-stocked shelves of the medical library. His return visit to Methodist Hospital was in 1958.

two years later joined the staff at Methodist. A personable young man with impeccable medical credentials, he maintained a successful obstetrics and gynecology practice for many years. In 1963, Dr. Lloyd would become Methodist's first full-time director of medical research.

Meanwhile, as a corollary to the nurse recruitment program, Methodist Hospital took steps in 1952 to further upgrade its school of nursing, which over the years had won high praise and was one of the hospital's great strengths. The decision to provide a stronger program grew out of a series of meetings involving Dr. Jerome C. Hixson, a hospital trustee and professor of English at DePauw University; Miss Fredericka Koch, director of the Methodist Hospital School of Nursing and nursing services; and Dean Robert Farber of the University. As a result, DePauw provided a visiting faculty for the Methodist school to give it a stronger academic base. Graduates of the Methodist school would not only be eligible to apply for a R.N. license but also earn academic credit toward a bachelor of science degree. One of the immediate results of the Methodist program was reflected in the annual examinations for licensing registered nurses—a higher percentage of Methodist nurses earned their license on the initial exam.

The success of the Methodist program had yet another result. DePauw University added a School

Shown above is the front page of the *Methodist Hospital Beacon's* first issue, January 1, 1954. The publication was the brainchild of James A. Stuart, editor *The Indianapolis Star* and public relations chairman of the Board of Trustees, and became a reality with the cooperation of Hospital Superintendent Jack A.L. Hahn. Florence Stone of the Hospital's public relations office was the *Beacon's* first editor.

of Nursing and invited Miss Koch to head up the school. Miss Koch agreed and for the next four years served as director of the university program as well as the Methodist Hospital School of Nursing. At the same time, Miss Koch continued as director of nursing services. Both schools took special pride in winning accreditation from the prestigious National League of Nursing.

In the same year the nursing program was being reorganized, a new publication, *The Methodist Hospital Beacon* was launched with the objective of providing improved communications at all levels of the hospital administration. A well edited four page newspaper, which later published six and eight page editions, the *Beacon* was the brainchild of James A. Stuart, editor of *The In-*

Dr. Paul K. Cullen, Medical Staff President, presenting a bronze plaque to Dr. Horace M. Banks commemorating 31 years' service as chief pathologist. Dr. Banks achieved international prominence for pioneering work and would develop a research laboratory to study cardiac surgery. Open heart surgery became a common procedure in the 1970s and led to the first heart transplant in a private hospital in 1982.

Miss Norma Baumann (standing), the first professional medical records librarian at Methodist Hospital, received the Governor's Distinguished Service Award in 1962 in recognition for her pioneering program of training and employing the blind as typists in the Medical Records Department. Shown here with blind typists (from L to R) Mr. Walter Johnson, unknown, and Miss Ruth Payne. At the time of her retirement in 1963, she had trained 15 blind typists and employed five.

dianapolis Star and chairman for public relations of the Board of Trustees, and became a reality with the cooperation of Superintendent Hahn. Florence Stone of the hospital's public relations office was the first editor. Thelma Hawthorne, administrative secretary whose 30-year tenure extended back to the days of Drs. Smith and Benson, handled circulation. The initial press run on January 1, 1954 was 7,500 copies.

Among the stories the *Beacon* covered in its first five years was the election of Arthur G. Wilson as president of the Board succeeding William G. Davis; the celebration of the 25th anniversary of the White Cross Guild; and the establishment of a special ward for premature babies. The publication took special pride in announcing that the hospital and its school of nursing and school of medical technology were fully accredited by the various accrediting organizations. Included was the training of interns and residents under the new medical education program.

During this period, the building program moved ahead. Ground was broken by William G. Davis, president of the Board of Trustees, in October of 1956 and by January of 1959 the new B plus building was opened. Late in 1956, the hospital purchased the Riley Hotel on the southeast corner of 16th Street and Capitol Avenue, to use as an exten-

sion of Wile Hall. The purchase of the hotel was an economy measure. Originally an addition to Wile Hall had been planned, but it was decided the purchase and renovation of the hotel would be less expensive. Officers of the Indianapolis Hospital Development Association concurred. In March of 1957 the first senior students moved into the building, which was named Wesley Hall, in honor of John Wesley, founder of Methodism. The new hall was used until 1978 when it was torn down and the land used for a parking lot. Later, in 1982, it was leased to the city for a key downtown station for the Indianapolis Fire Department, an ideal arrangement since it assured virtually next door fire protection for the hospital.

A new resident and intern complex of apartments was built north of Wile Hall and named the Eberwein-Claypool Wetzel Apartments in honor of its donors—Dr. John H. Eberwein, one of the first physicians to perform surgery at Methodist, and the estate of Anna Claypool Wetzel.

Other gifts and endowments came in including $250,000 from the Ford Foundation to supplement IHDA funds. All were welcome and more were solicited as it appeared that, over and above the funds provided by the IHDA, an additional $2,000,000 would be required to carry out Methodist Hospital's extensive building and expansion program. Jack Hahn stressed that no gift was

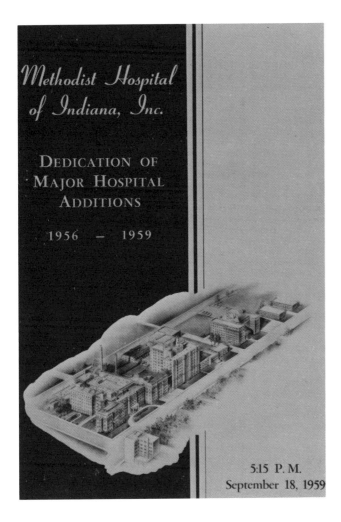

5:15 P. M.
September 18, 1959

Cover of the September 18, 1959 Dedication Program. Bishop Richard C. Raines was the principal speaker and dedicated the new 208-bed general hospital, the expanded center wing and the new C-Building. Arthur G. Wilson, president of the Board of Trustees, presided. (Methodist Hospital Archives.)

too small, citing a patient gift of two electric fans, a $50 contribution from a Presbyterian church for "free service" use, and $10 gifts from a sixth grade class in Morgan County and a Women's Society in Franklin.

While construction was underway, there was a new development in the Methodist program. Under the IHDA program, financing was provided for Methodist, the new Community Hospital, St. Francis Hospital and Norways Foundation Psychiatric Hospital, a privately owned psychiatric facility. Norways, however, found itself in planning and financial difficulties. IHDA requested Methodist Hospital to take over the program and the hospital agreed, expanding the limited psychiatric program at Methodist. The 1B 32-bed nursing unit continued to serve as a "closed" psychiatric unit while plans were developed for a C Building which would care for 107 patients.

The building program was climaxed on September 18, 1959 when the new major additions to Methodist Hospital were formally dedicated and opened to patients. Arthur G. Wilson, president of the Board of Trustees presided, and Methodist Bishop Richard C. Raines formally dedicated the new 208-bed general hospital unit, expansion of the center wing and the new C Building. Other speakers included Indianapolis Mayor Charles Boswell, IHDA Board Chairman, and IHDA President Edward F. Gallahue.

In his dedicatory remarks Bishop Raines stressed the hospital's insistence on "the highest standards of medical practice" and reiterated that Methodist Hospital was open to all races and creeds and to the poor as well as to the rich without distinction.

"Methodist Hospital," he said, "is a house of worship—not through ritual, robes and sermons, but through deeds of love and mercy. Christ made sensitiveness to suffering and the will to inconvenience one's self to help alleviate suffering the touchstone of acceptablilty of God when He said, 'Come ye blessed to my Father, for I was sick and ye visited me and inasmuch as ye did it unto one of the least of these, ye did it unto me.'"

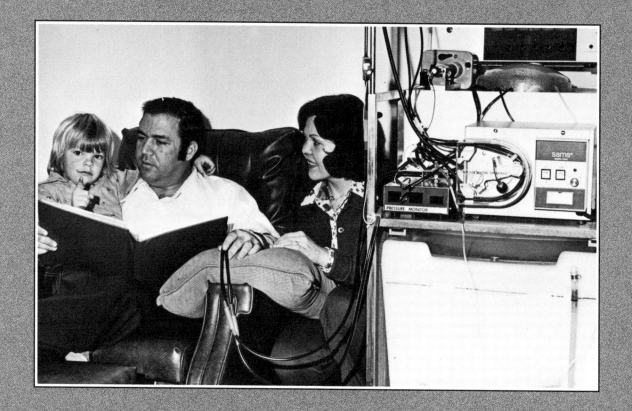

Chapter Eleven

Triumphs and Tragedies

"Where the spirit of Christ shines forth from the lives of those who serve and where the finest scientific medicine is practiced, there and there alone is the ultimate in the healing art achieved. It is this ultimate toward which Methodist Hospital can and should be a house of worship through the deeds of love and mercy."
—Bishop Richard C. Raines
Ground-Breaking Commemorative
Remarks October, 1956

O n May 23, 1960, one week before the annual Indianapolis 500 Mile Race, Methodist Hospital staged its first rehearsal of a disaster drill as part of the local Civil Defense program. As Jack Hahn remembered it, the drill was "a catastrophe...everything we did was wrong. But it taught us something." A week later, on the day of the race, while hospital officials were still smarting over the drill's deficiencies, a real disaster occurred at the Speedway.

Like all disasters, the one at the Speedway was sudden and unexpected. A makeshift scaffolding five stories high packed with race fans and built on the top of a truck parked in the infield, collapsed during the pace lap. Men and women were hurled to the ground, some pinned beneath the steel framework. Two persons were killed instantly and more than 60 others were injured.

A spectator at the race, Jack Hahn rushed to the emergency Speedway Hospital where the dead and injured had been taken and Dr. Thomas Hanna, medical director, and Barbara Webb, director of the nursing staff, were preparing the injured for removal to Methodist Hospital. Hahn rode back to Indianapolis in one of the six ambulances and two station wagons that carried patients to Methodist for treatment. At the hospital, all was efficiency in sharp contrast to the previous week's rehearsal.

A newspaper reporter described the scene at Methodist:

"When the injured arrived at Methodist, everything was ready. All of the hospital carts and wheel chairs were already lined up in the corridor next to the receiving ward when the ambulances arrived. All available male personnel at the hospital

Patient and wife learn to use hemodialysis equipment under the direction of a Methodist Hospital technician. Hemodialysis procedures have been performed in patients' homes since the 1960s.

111

had been obtained as orderlies. In 40 minutes more than fifty patients were brought into Methodist—but 'there was never a jam,' Hahn said. 'Although the hospital has 12 diagnostic X-ray rooms, at times there were 25 seriously ill patients in the department, on carts or wheel chairs awaiting X-ray examination or final diagnosis from the film for further treatment,' he explained. He credited a technician on duty with the presence of mind to warm up the automatic processing and developing machine making it possible for X-ray films to be 'developed and interpreted in a matter of minutes in a truly assembly line procedure.'

"Part of the disaster plan was to insure there would be no elevator blockage caused by other than emergency patients using the self operating elevators. Disaster stations of the hospital porters were to stand guard at those elevators.

"Hahn said the only elevator problem occurred 'when a patient with a broken back had been placed on a board by the Speedway Hospital. The board did not fit into the elevator and it was necessary to call a maintenance man to saw off the end of the board before the patient could be transferred to the shock room and surgery.'

"By 3:30 p.m. less than an hour after the end of the big race, the X-ray and minor surgery races were over at Methodist. Surgery finished its last case at 10:00 p.m. In all, twenty-nine patients were admitted. None died. But 12 were still in the hospital last night. The disaster plan not only included treatment, it also included an 'information center' where anxious friends and relatives could await word of victims' conditions without impeding the treatment operations.

"A runner was used to carry the word from the hospital to the White Cross Center auditorium adjacent to the hospital which was the information center. A log of all the injured—name, address, age, injury and general condition—was kept up to date and relayed to the information center and to the press."

In all, it was a proud moment for Methodist Hospital.

The Speedway disaster occurred at a time when the hospital was again facing crowded conditions. Despite the ambitious building program of the 1950s, the demand for hospital care continued unabated and Indianapolis was still desperately short of beds—1,300 of them according to the local administrator of the federal Hill-Burton program. At Methodist, Jack Hahn, his title now executive director, reported in April of 1961, "There is continual pressure for admission of adult medical and surgical patients and...many rooms have extra beds and often elective patients with long standing reservations have been sent home when adequate beds were not available. This we believe to be a better answer than placing patients in corridors or lounges where it is difficult to render good care and where accommodations and service are criticized."

He also reported a record admission of 33,325 patients during 1960, "which to the best of our knowledge is the largest of any directly church related hospital in the United States." The daily patient average was also a new record: 775 patients.

Opening of a new two-story addition to the South Wing with its 50 beds failed to alleviate the critical shortage. Designed as an out-patient building, the new unit also provided a new main entrance on 16th Street, giving the hospital three entrances and an equal number of lobbies. The new beds on Main South were assigned to diabetic patients in a continuation of Methodist's lead in the treatment of diabetes begun in 1922.

In April of 1963 the hospital opened its first Intensive Care Unit (ICU) with 19 beds on 5-A. As its name implied, the unit was devoted to patients requiring intensive and special care for severe illnesses, heart conditions and injuries. Indicative of the special care provided in the unit was the nurse-patient ratio—two nurses for each patient. During its first six weeks of operation, 91 patients were admitted with an average stay of four and one-half days. No one could foresee in those early months the important and critical role the intensive care unit would play in October of the same year when the hospital would be called upon to cope with another major disaster.

To hospital administrators the 1960s appeared to be a replay of the previous decade for, in addition to shortages of beds and overcrowded conditions, they continued to wrestle with the problem

In April, 1963, Methodist Hospital opened its first intensive care unit (ICU) with 19 beds on 5-A devoted to patients requiring intensive and special care for severe illnesses, heart conditions and injuries. Today there are five separate ICU's equipped with the most modern technology and headed by specially qualified physicians. They are: coronary critical care, adult ICU, open heart recovery, neuro constant care, and pediatric ICU — for a total of 68 beds.

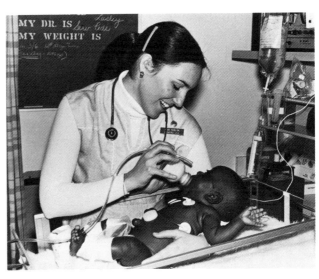

Angie Read, R.N., feeding one of her tiny charges in the Pediatric Intensive Care Unit of Methodist Hospital. House officers and Methodist residents are assigned to the ICU 24 hours a day and each nurse cares for a single patient or a maximum of two. About 15 per cent of the 4,000 babies born each year in the Regional Center for Mothers and Babies are treated in the special care nursery. Most are treated for abnormalities associated with premature birth.

of inflation, spiraling costs and a critical shortage of nurses. At Methodist, new efforts were made to recruit R.N.s, particularly for the less desirable evening and night shifts. Although the nursing school continued to enroll record numbers, too many of the school's graduates were going elsewhere after graduation. This was also true of nursing faculty sent off to school to earn graduate degrees.

To attract more nurses, the $235 tuition fee for the senior year at the Methodist School of Nursing and at the DePauw School of Nursing was waived if the new graduate would agree to serve on the nursing staff of Methodist for one year. Methodist also obtained funding from the Methodist Conferences for nursing scholarships. These were awarded to young ladies who also would agree to stay at Methodist for at least one year after graduation. As yet another step to alleviate the shortage, extra training was given the Pink Ladies of the White Cross Guild and a program inaugurated "to encourage and utilize their services...on the evening and night shifts."

The hospital tackled another problem that made staffing the night shifts difficult—the lack of on-campus housing or housing immediately adjacent to the hospital. During the early 1960s, it purchased a 17-unit apartment building on West 18th Street and entered into an agreement in 1963 with

the Shiel-Sexton Corporation for construction of a 54-unit Chateau Apartment complex on 20th Street, bordering on Senate Avenue. The completed units were also managed and maintained by the builder until the hospital exercised an option to buy them. Upon purchasing them, the Chateau complex was remodeled and renamed the Arthur G. Wilson Quadrangle in recognition of Mr. Wilson's service as president of the Board of Trustees from 1958-1961 and his role in negotiating the the the purchase of additional properties for campus expansion.

Inflation was also taking its toll and pushing up hospital rates. Although the inflation of the 1960s would not begin to compare with the double digit figures of the 1970s, it was having an effect on wages and the cost of hospital supplies. Methodist was forced, albeit reluctantly, to increase room rates by $2 a day to offset rising wage costs. The hospital also cited the 40-hour work week, which was now in effect in all Indianapolis hospitals (and in 80% of the nation's hospitals) as another cost factor. The shorter work week required the hiring of additional employees.

In 1967 hospital employees were covered, for the first time, under the Fair Labor Standards Act which fixed minimum wages at $1.00 an hour and

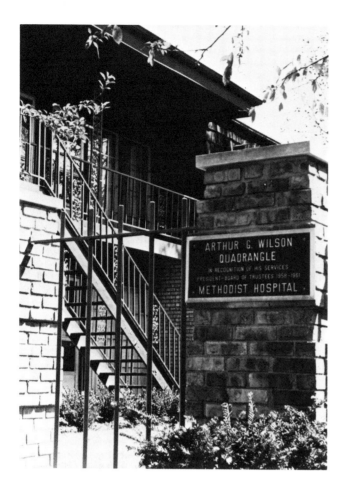

Marking the start of Methodist Hospital's $6.5 million expansion program in 1967, a giant crane sends a 2,000-pound steel ball smashing into the stone columns of the original hospital entrance. (Indianapolis News Photo, Horace Ketring.)

Board President Arthur G. Wilson, 1958-1961, was recognized by the Board for leadership in acquisition of land and properties for hospital expansion by naming the apartment complex for medical and nursing personnel at 20th Street and Senate Avenue, the Arthur G. Wilson Quadrangle.

provided for a fifteen cent an hour increase in successive years. The starting wage at Methodist was more than the national minimum, $1.23 an hour, and this was raised to $1.40 with the start of the new fiscal year, July 1, 1967. Later it rose to $1.71 per hour. The reason given for paying more than the minimum wage was the hospital's desire to be competitive in the wage market and to obtain competent employees to provide staffing for quality patient care. At the same time, starting pay for registered nurses was $325 a month with bonuses ranging from $25 to $40 for those who worked the evening and night shifts. Top pay after five years of service was $400 monthly.

As inflation continued to spiral, the hospital took steps to reduce operating costs and improve worker efficiency. In 1961, on the recommendation of the board's executive committee, a con-

sulting firm was hired to analyze work patterns and services. The firm's recommendations resulted in savings of several hundred thousand dollars. To further increase productivity a methods engineer was appointed, forerunner of an expanded department of industrial engineering. Meanwhile, the Board of Trustees and Controller Chester M. Warman were instituting procedures to provide tighter fiscal control.

Renovation of the older hospital buildings, underway since the end of World War II, continued unabated and in 1960 alone—called the "Year of Remodeling"—the hospital spent $1,235,833 for building renovation, new equipment and the installation of air conditioning systems. Air conditioning had been included in the new buildings erected during the 1950s and now the system was being extended to the older structures. As for new equipment, the phenomenal advances and changes in medical science and technology dictated frequent replacements to maintain Methodist's standard of excellence.

In addition to providing patient care, Methodist was also a "teaching" hospital with increasing

Methodist Hospital Chaplain the Rev. Dr. Claude M. McClure comforts a bereaved couple in the quiet of the hospital's chapel. Dr. McClure, who estimated he made over a quarter of a million bedside visits during his 14-year chaplaincy, retired in 1961. He was succeeded by the hospital's first certified professional hospital chaplain, the Rev. Dr. Kenneth E. Reed.

educational responsibilities. As many as 600 students each year participated in several accredited programs: School of Nursing; rotating medical internship; residency training in eight clinical specialities; chaplaincy internship and residency; hospital administration residency; School of Medical Technology (affiliated with four colleges); School of X-ray Technology; courses in Clinical Pastoral Education in cooperation with Garrett Biblical Institute and Christian Theological Seminary; affiliates for clinical experience from the Indianapolis School of Practical Nursing; and a cooperating relationship with the DePauw School of Nursing.

The hospital's medical education program was growing and expanding under the leadership of Dr. Jack H. Hall with the cooperation and support of a succession of medical staff presidents that included Drs. Lawson J. Clark, Glen V. Ryan, Louis W.

Nie, Arnold J. Bachman and Donald E. Stephens. As a corollary to the new emphasis on medical education at Methodist, more and more interns and residents were applying for admission. In 1962-63 the highest number of applications in the hospital's history were received, 72 for a quota of 20 positions. At the same time, outpatient services increased from 39,000 in 1951 to 235,000 patients in 1961.

During this period, hospital executives watched with interest a contest of wills between two strong personalities at the top—Daniel F. Evans, elected president of the Board of Trustees in 1965, and Jack Hahn, executive director (superintendent). Evans and Hahn, although they did not always see eye to eye, represented one of the strongest partnerships in the history of the hospital. Both men were young, positive, intelligent—and committed. Both knew hospital management on a first hand basis and each came well prepared to defend his point of view at meetings of the Board of Directors. Evans, a Board member for many years and president of L.S. Ayres & Co., brought a solid business and financial background to his post. He was also the third generation to serve on the Methodist Board as his grandfather and great-grandfather had been Board members before him.

While Evans and Hahn were not always in agreement, each respected the other's point of view and both not only abided by the decisions of the Board of Trustees, but worked hard to carry out its mandates. Evans' position was that the hospital "could not be all things to all people" while Hahn was a strong advocate of expanded hospital services designed to serve the maximum number of people. At a time when new hospital services were being rapidly developed and services were pro-

liferating, the men served to counter balance each other.

New emphasis was placed on the hospital's chaplaincy program with the appointment in 1958 of 30-year old Dr. Kenneth E. Reed as an associate to Dr. Claude M. McClure, senior chaplain at Methodist. Dr. Reed inaugurated several non-denominational programs in spiritual care for seminary students as well as ministers, doctors and nurses. Established as a program designed to treat "the whole person," these classes marked the beginning of a new emphasis on spiritual, psychological and physical healing which, in the late 1970s would be called "wholistic medicine." When Dr. McClure retired in 1961, after 14 years as chaplain of Methodist Hospital, Dr. Reed, the first certified professional hospital chaplain at Methodist, was appointed director of chaplaincy

Dedication of the Mary Hanson Carey Chapel, January 24, 1963. Standing to the left of one of the two inspiring stained glass windows are: (l. to r.) the Rev. Kenneth E. Reed, Director, Chaplaincy Services; the Rev. Jean S. Milner of the Board of Trustees; and Bishop Richard C. Raines. At right is Jack A.L. Hahn, superintendent of Methodist Hospital (Indianapolis News Photo, George Tilford.)

Methodist Hospital officials proudly displayed a plaque and a portrait of Bishop Richard C. Raines, which was installed at the entrance of a new board room named for the bishop in honor of his 20 years of active participation on the Board of Trustees. Standing at the left in this 1967 photo are: Jack Hahn, superintendent of Methodist Hospital and Bishop and Mrs. Raines. Standing at right are: Mrs. Francis Hughes, Mr. Hughes, a member of the Board of Trustees; and Daniel F. Evans, president of the Board of Trustees.

service. Dr. McClure, who estimated he made over a quarter of a million bedside visits during his chaplaincy, moved to Greencastle to serve as parish visitor on the staff of the Gobin Methodist Church where he had once been minister.

Aided by grants from Lilly Endowment and the Paul H. Buchanan family of Indianapolis and given the full and unqualified support of the Board of Trustees, the chaplaincy and pastoral education programs became one of the hospital's most successful activities. A symbol of the hospital's recognition of the value of spiritual help in the process of getting well, the program was divided into three basic units each headed by a qualified and trained ministerial associate: Pastoral Care, Pastoral Education and the Buchanan Counseling Center. The program established ministerial internships and residencies, conducted workshops for pastors and developed a program of pastoral care and family counseling in the Neighborhood

Health Centers. The educational program for seminary students and pastors took on an international and interdenominational flavor for it not only attracted large numbers of students from all over the United States, but also from Canada, Sweden, Australia, Ireland and other European and Asiatic nations. The pastoral education programs which carried academic credit, attracted national attention and won the accreditation of the Institute of Pastoral Care (later the Association for Clinical Pastoral Education). One of the immediate results of the program at Methodist was the establishment of a pastoral visitation program on a 24-hour-a-day basis, seven days a week, and in 1967 the appointment of the hospital's first full-time Catholic chaplain, Father William S. Fisher. It was also a policy that a chaplain was to visit with the family of every patient who died at the hospital.

The Buchanan Counseling Center, a gift of Paul

H. Buchanan, Sr., chairman of the Board of Directors of Flanner & Buchanan Mortuaries, and family, was formally dedicated on October 4, 1968 by Bishop Reuben H. Mueller, resident bishop of the United Methodist Church. The new center enabled the chaplaincy service to expand its already extensive programs in counseling and religious ministry and to offer counseling to the Indianapolis community as well as patients at Methodist. For pastors and seminary students, it provided a clinical setting in which they could improve their counseling skills. The general professionalism of the Buchanan Center's program quickly earned wide respect and later the accreditation of the American Association of Pastoral Counselors.

A new and enlarged Mary Hanson Carey Memorial Chapel was opened in 1961 and located in the heart of the hospital, dominating the main entrance. The new chapel, as with many hospital innovations, was made possible by a spontaneous outpouring of gifts by employees, former patients, hospital trustees, nursing school alumnae, White Cross Guild, individual Guild members and countless private citizens. Originally established by a gift from Mrs. Carey in 1933, the enlarged chapel incorporated seating for 55 persons and space for wheel chairs. According to a writer in the *Beacon,* the new chapel was designed to "bring comfort in many ways to countless persons throughout the years, even as the present chapel has been a source of comfort and inspiration." Like the original chapel, the new chapel incorporated symbols of the Protestant, Catholic and Jewish faiths and provided "a place for meditation and worship for all persons."

Two inspiring stained glass windows, each in dramatic color portraying the healing Christ, were among the Chapel's outstanding features. One of the four by six foot windows greeted visitors coming through Methodist's main entrance; the other faced into the chapel. The specially designed lights were of the same stained glass and were donated by Josephine Stout, a deaconess-nurse who had been employed for many years in anesthesiology. Nurse Stout had also helped develop the hospital's weekly chapel services. The new chapel was dedicated on January 24, 1963 by Bishop Richard C. Raines of the Indiana Area of the Methodist Church. Dr. Reed presided at the dedicatory services and Francis M. Hughes, president of the Board of Trustees, and other hospital officials par-

ticipated. Former Chaplain Claude McClure gave the invocation.

The vacated chapel was later refurbished and converted to the Bishop Richard C. Raines Board Room in honor of Bishop Raines' 20 years of active participation on the Board of Trustees. A picture of the bishop and a plaque were installed at the entrance. The plaque incorporated a quotation from the bishop's dedicatory address in October of 1956: "Where the spirit of Christ shines forth from the lives of those who serve and where the finest scientific medicine is practiced, there and there alone is the ultimate in the healing art achieved. It is this ultimate toward which Methodist Hospital can and should be a house of worship through deeds of love and mercy."

Formal presentation of the board room took place on April 28, 1967 and Daniel F. Evans, president of the hospital Board, not only praised Bishop Raines for his years of service, but credited the bishop for his key roles in such "vital matters as hospital accreditation, the emphasis on physician responsibility for patient care, the identification of the risks in federal financing, and the desirability of avoiding any impression of narrow denominationalism."

The new chapel, the expanded chaplaincy service and the Buchanan Counseling Center were in keeping with the hospital's continuing objective to introduce the spirit of the church into the hospital's daily activities. As Jack Hahn wrote in his monthly column in *The Methodist Hospital Beacon*: "The patient and the student coming to the church related hospital have the right to expect a relationship and an understanding based on high standards of human relations religiously motivated. While the church should not use the hospital as a source of evangelism, the principles of human relations in the doctrine of the Church should be expected to govern not only the care of patients, but the interpersonal relationships within the institution."

In the same year that Methodist dedicated its new Mary Hanson Carey Chapel, Indianapolis suffered the worst tragedy in its history—a tragedy that found Methodist Hospital again prepared and ready; its disaster plan again functioning smoothly and efficiently.

The tragedy occurred on Halloween night, in the Coliseum at the Indiana State Fairgrounds as an audience of 4,327 persons, most of them families with children, sat watching the finale of the Holi-

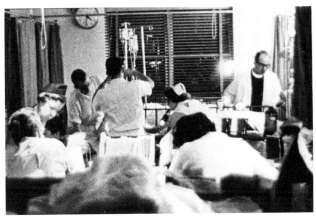

Methodist Hospital's intensive care unit on the night of the Coliseum tragedy. Shown here with victims of the disaster are doctors, graduate and student nurses, a public health nurse, who volunteered her services, and Hospital Chaplain Paul Stavrakos. (Indianapolis News Photo.)

Concern, pressure, shock - all are reflected on the face of Jack Hahn, Methodist Hospital's executive director in this candid photo taken on the night of the Coliseum tragedy. Upon learning of the explosion at the State Fairgrounds, Hahn mobilized the Methodist staff and put the hospital's disaster plan into effect. Methodist Hospital treated 120 patients and admitted 65 of the disaster victims.

day on Ice Show. Leaking butane gas that had been collecting under a section of the seats exploded, hurling screaming men, women and children onto the ice. Hissing yellow-orange flames poured from the jagged crater left by the explosion.

There was a moment of panic, but miraculously the crowd gained control of itself and flowed out of the hall. Even as the first of the crowd emerged into the chill October air, police, fire and ambulance sirens punctuated the night. Outside the Coliseum, the grounds resembled a battlefield with scores of injured to be treated and taken by ambulances to the city's hospitals.

Upon hearing the news, Executive Director Jack Hahn declared the hospital's disaster plan in effect and the hospital mobilized for action. When the

first disaster victims arrived at 11:20 p.m., doctors of the 50-member House Staff were already at their duty posts. Physicians of the attending staff and off-duty personnel were pouring into the hospital —voluntarily. The emergency room became a "triage" or sorting area. One hundred and ten of the victims were sent to X-ray; 42 were sent to the surgery recovery room which doubled as a shock treatment center or post-surgery area. Twenty-three persons were operated on before 6 a.m. Most of the injuries were serious; there were no ambulatory patients. In all, Methodist treated 120 patients and admitted 65, some of whom would remain in the hospital for months. Said one physician, "It reminded me of the war."

In retrospect, it was an all-out effort. Eighteen people worked through the night setting up 60 blood transfusions. A radio appeal was made for more blood donors and more than 250, most of them teenagers, lined up to volunteer their services. Hundreds of others had to be turned away. Junior and senior student nurses joined with hospital R.N.s in caring for patients. Members of the social service, purchasing, pharmacy, personnel, medical records and controller's departments were mobilized. The dietary department served 55 gallons of coffee in six different areas. Maintenance and security departments cooperated in guarding doors. The admitting department assigned patients to intensive care units, rooms, halls and even some to the obstetrical unit. White Cross volunteers assisted in providing information.

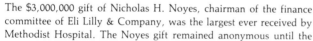

The $3,000,000 gift of Nicholas H. Noyes, chairman of the finance committee of Eli Lilly & Company, was the largest ever received by Methodist Hospital. The Noyes gift remained anonymous until the new Children's Pavilion was completed and Mr. Noyes announced it was a tribute to his wife, Marguerite Lilly Noyes.

Others, who had had training, assisted with patients. All six of the chaplaincy staff were on duty, ministering to the spiritual needs of the injured and dying. Relatives and friends of disaster victims were directed to the White Cross Service Center, where additional phones were set up to provide up-to-date information on patients and their conditions.

The statistics of the city's worst tragedy were grim: within weeks its death toll reached 74 men, women and children, its list of injured well over 300. Methodist Hospital also suffered a personal loss. Two of its employees, Gwendolyn Campbell and Lois E. Groover were among those killed as was Dr. James Staten, a member of the medical staff, and his wife and a son. Another son was hospitalized at Methodist. Numbered among the many members of the hospital family who were injured was Dr. James H. Gosman, later to become president of the hospital's medical staff.

The Coliseum tragedy helped to underscore the fact that Indianapolis was woefully short of hospital beds. A Hill-Burton report quoted in *The Indianapolis Times* said it considered a rate of 75% patient occupancy a reasonable figure, but said 80 percent was "tight" and 85 percent placed a hospital "under pressure." At Methodist the occupancy rate in medical/surgical was 92.1 and in obstetrics, 85.75 percent. Individual patients were frequently re-examined to see if their stay could be shortened and Blue Cross adopted a policy requiring member doctors to sign re-confirmation of a patient's hospitalization if the patient were confined more than 15 days. A major part of Methodist's problem lay in the fact that, aside from drawing its patients from a growing and expanding metropolis, it was also attracting patients, generally referrals, from all over Indiana and neighboring states. This had always been true, even during the hospital's early days, but in the early 1960s more than 40 percent of Methodist's patients were from out of the city. A compliment to the excellence of

Methodist's staff and modern facilities, it was a major contributing factor to the hospital's continuing shortage of patient beds.

The problem, however, took a dramatic turn in the early and mid 1960s with the anouncement of a series of large and generous gifts for new hospital buildings and a second drive for funds by the Indianapolis Hospital Development Association. In its announcement of a new public campaign for funds, the association reported that a study it had commissioned showed that Indianapolis would need 2,000 more hospital beds by 1970. A goal of $15,500,000 was established of which $4,600,000 was earmarked for Methodist Hospital in order to bring the institution's bed count up to 1,200. The gifts and the IHDA funds resulted in the largest single building program in the hospital's history.

Two of the hospital's gifts were magnanimous: those of Herman C. Krannert, chairman of the board of the Inland Container Corporation, and Mrs. Krannert, who gave the hospital $800,000 and Nicholas H. Noyes, chairman of the finance committee of Eli Lilly and Company, whose gift of $3,000,000 was the largest ever received at the hospital. The Noyes gift remained anonymous until the new Children's Pavilion was completed and dedicated in October of 1967 when Mr. Noyes was revealed as the donor. "The Children's Pavilion," he said, "has been built not only to help children but as a tribute to a wonderful woman, who all her life has been interested in the welfare of children, Marguerite Lilly Noyes, to whom I have been happily engaged and married for more than 60 years."

With funds now available for expansion, Methodist immediately embarked on a $13.8 million construction program which included:

> The Krannert Tower on the 16th Street side of the hospital which fulfilled a multiplicity of needs including patient care areas for the hospital's urological service (said to be the largest in the nation); new post-partum obstetrical facilities; beds for general surgical patients with special conveniences for parents and concerned families; a special unit designed to render care in an atmosphere geared to the complete comfort of the patient as well as facilitating quality care by physicians and nurses.

> The new seven-story 114-bed Children's Pavilion dedicated to Mrs. Noyes, design-

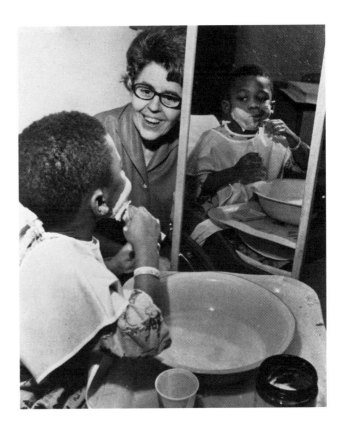

Evaluating patients' emotional and physical responses through play, Mrs. Rona Krause, play therapist at Methodist Hospital, watches as four-year-old Marc Jackson shaves "just like daddy." Mrs. Krause, a very innovative person, was known for years as Methodist's "Play Lady." One of her creative ideas was Krefcha, a medical play doll designed by her and other employees, used to let children "draw blood." Through playing doctor or nurse they alleviate many of their anxieties and better cope with hospitalization. The Alpha Pi Omega Sorority and a White Cross Guild member make the approximately 100 dolls used annually. (Indianapolis Star Photo by William A. Oates)

ed for infants and children up to 14 years of age.

A six-story $2,100,000 addition to the C Building to provide beds for 172 medical and surgical patients, 41 psychiatric patients and 26 patients with contagious diseases—a net increase of 128 beds after renovation, expansion of services and transfer of the children's beds to the new Pavilion.

A six-story $2,200,000 professional services center wing for laboratory, X-ray and surgical facilities.

And a $310,000 Nuclear Medicine Center which would house the latest scientific weapons in the fight against cancer including a new Cobalt 60 radio isotope.

In addition, a 412-car parking garage was planned at 18th and Capitol, on the site of the former apartment house for nurses, to help alleviate a shortage of parking space.

Construction of the new buildings was started at once and most were completed during the years 1965, 1967 and 1968. A new wing addition costing $6,500,000 was completed in 1969. One of the new six-story wings, the new front wing, changed the basic appearance of Methodist's main building and entrance for the first time since the fourth floor was added in 1917. Meanwhile, modernization of older areas of the hospital continued and the trustees set 1974 as a date for completion of the extensive renovation program which had been underway since the end of World War II. Most of the modernization programs were carried out by construction crews of the hospital maintenance department and at considerable savings to the hospital.

Opportunity for the hospital's future growth received major assistance in 1968 when the Metropolitan Planning Commission, recognizing the needs of hospitals and related services, secured passage of a zoning ordinance permitting the establishment of hospital districts as part of a Comprehensive Plan for Marion County. The ordinance, believed to be the first of its kind, represented the joint effort of the Commission staff and Methodist Hospital administrators. The Methodist Hospital District became the first and only district recognized under the new ordinance.

With the growing number of gifts, endowments, bequests and grants to the hospital, from its supporters, former patients, businesses and foundations, and the continuing need to raise additional funds, the Board, in 1961, established and incorporated the Methodist Hospital Foundation which became the fund raising arm of the hospital. The Foundation, made up of corporate and community leaders, was also pledged to sponsor "specific projects and programs to improve Methodist Hospital's service to its patients and...to promote the general health of the public and to encourage, support and promote the hospital's education, training and research programs."

Francis M. Hughes, a member of the hospital Board of Trustees, who would serve as hospital board president and a trustee for 30 years, was elected president of the Foundation. A prominent attorney and civic leader, he had played an impor-

Philanthropist, Herman C. Krannert, chairman of the board of the Inland Container Corporation, whose $800,000 gift made possible the Krannert Tower on 16th Street.

tant role in helping to arrange the $3,000,000 gift from Mr. Nicholas Noyes for the Children's Pavilion. Hughes would serve as president of the Foundation for the next 20 years.

The new department of Medical Research under Dr. Frank P. Lloyd, and his associate, Judith A. Barrett, R.N., was in the forefront of emerging developments in medicine. Among the most dramatic was the use of an artificial kidney in 1966 —one of the first of its type in the country. Financed initially by a $15,000 grant from M. Lila Lilly and the Indianapolis Foundation, the program, one of 12 underway in the United States, was later granted an award of $445,684 by the United States Public Health Service to continue research development and study the feasibility of home dialysis. As a result a Hemodialysis Department was established at Methodist under the direction of Dr. George W. Applegate and during 1969 performed 4,289 hemodialysis procedures including 3,073 performed in patients' homes. The artificial kidney program was one more example of reversing a terminal illness and returning a patient to a productive home and community life. Statistics help tell the story: nationally, in 1965, 11,920 per 100,000 persons died from kidney failure; in 1975, the toll had been reduced to 8,072 per 100,000.

Another example of saving lives was the first open heart surgeries at Methodist—again a program developed by Medical Research. Today, open heart and by-pass surgery are commonplace, but in 1960 such an operation was a real breakthrough and the first step toward the most dramatic of all heart surgeries—the heart transplant.

Open heart surgery was the result of two years of research on animals and the continuing rehearsal and perfection of techniques by a selected team of physicians and technicians. All were aware that earlier surgery, performed by Dr. J.V. Thompson in the 1950s, had been less than successful and Dr. Thompson had abandoned the idea. The new team, however, persisted.

The first open heart surgeries were performed successfully in 1965 by a team consisting of Drs. John Pittman, Harry Siderys and Gilbert Herod, the latter a resident at Methodist. Barbara Hall was anesthetist and the technical assistants were Ronald Polk, James Twitty and George Berry, who acted as profusionist during the research phase of preparation. Assisting in the operations were nurses Ruth Perkins and Cathy Ruby.

More operations followed and in 1971 Methodist Hospital became one of a select few medical centers—actually only 30 in the United States —performing open heart surgery on a daily basis. By 1972 the Methodist team had performed about 200 heart valve operations including repair and replacement of damaged valves. The figure also included repair of aneurysms and congential defects. A new technique—coronary vein bypass grafts that used a section of the saphenous vein of the patient's leg—became common. Methodist later reported some 300 of these operations had been performed by staff physicians.

For heart patients there was also a new hospital unit—a new seven-bed coronary care unit—the gift of Mr. and Mrs. H. Richard Howard of Indianapolis, whose daughter had once undergone heart surgery at Methodist. It was a welcome addition for the hospital was treating 700 to 800 heart

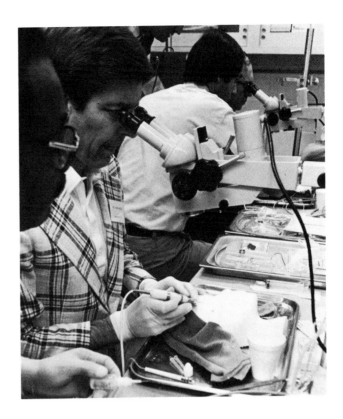

The Vitreous Surgery Clinic of the Medical Research Laboratory is shown in this 1980 photograph.

patients a year. The new unit's sophisticated equipment included an electrocardiographic monitor and an electronic pacemaker to stimulate the heart. When it became operational in 1966, the unit lowered dramatically the mortality rate for coronary occlusions.

A program that would bring national recognition was begun in 1964 by Dr. Lewis C. Robbins in collaboration with Dr. Jack H. Hall and under the auspices of the Medical Education Department. Titled "Pilot Project in Health Hazard Programming," the program, a branch of prospective medicine, correlated a person's medical history, health, and lifestyle with mortality rates and computed the risk of dying from various causes in the next ten years. As the result of Drs. Robbins' and Hall's efforts, Methodist Hospital received the Gerard B. Lambert Award in 1972—a recognition of the hospital's leadership in the development of the prospective medicine concept.

Methodist Hospital was also reaching out into the Indianapolis community to bring medical services to targeted inner city areas by way of

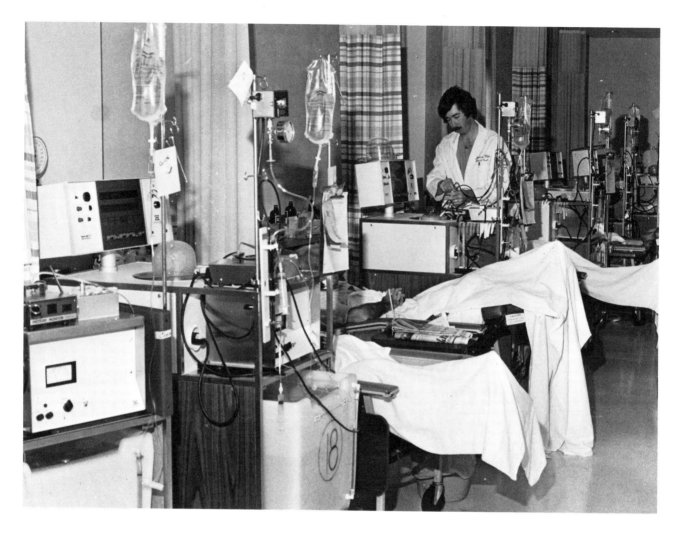

Methodist Hospital's Hemodialysis Unit. The hospital's use of an artificial kidney, one of the first of its type in the nation, was among the dramatic developments in medicine in 1966. Three years later Methodist established a hemodialysis department under the direction of Dr. George W. Applegate. During 1969 the unit performed 4,289 hemodialysis procedures.

neighborhood health centers. These centers had been inaugurated as the result of the concerns of two Methodist ministers, the Reverend L. Ray Sells of the Fletcher Place Church and the Reverend Gerald Trigg, pastor of the Central Avenue Church. The two ministers had organized a march on the South Indiana Annual Conference in 1968 and presented a formal request that Methodist Hospital develop health centers within the boundaries of their neighborhoods. The ministers pointed out that although the combined census tracts counted 40,000 people in their area, most of them subsisting at the poverty level, only one doctor, and he was in semi-retirement, practiced in the area. The ministers also cited the problems encountered by people in the area in arranging transportation to Marion County General Hospital

(now Wishard) and the long waits that occurred after they had arrived at the out-patient clinics.

With the approval of the Indiana Conference and the cooperation of Methodist's Board of Trustees, the first two of these centers, the Southeast Health Center (Fletcher Place) and the Central Avenue Health Center, were launched in 1968 with Dr. Dale S. Benson, a young and deeply religious physician, as medical director. A report at the beginning of 1970 showed a total of 10,310 patient visits with 60 percent of the patients under 18 years of age. The success of the centers in helping the needy, prompted the establishment in 1972 of a third center, the Southwest Health Center, at 2202 West Morris Street. Representing an expression of concern on behalf of Methodist Hospital for people regardless of their income, the centers

A pilot project in health hazard programming under the leadership of Drs. Lewis C. Robbins and Jack H. Hall correlated a person's medical history, health and lifestyle with mortality rates and computed the risk of dying from various diseases in the next ten years. Methodist Hospital was the first in the country to use risk factors in early disease management and effective prevention. Shown here during a national conference in 1964 are (L. to R.) Dr. Marilyn Sanders; Dr. Joseph Sadusk, Director of Federal Food and Drug Administration; Dr. Robbins; a Senior Medical Student Assistant; Dr. Loren Martin; Dr. Hall; and Dr. Donald E. Stephens. Methodist Hospital received the Gerard B. Lambert Award in 1972 in recognition of leadership in developing this concept.

provided clinic hours in general medicine, pediatrics and other medical specialties. Chaplains and pastoral counselors were also assigned to the centers and counseling became an important part of the center's continuing services. The neighborhood centers were, in a very real sense, following in the steps of John Wesley who had established dispensaries in poor neighborhoods in the 18th century.

Rated by the Department of Health and Human Services as "best" in this section of the country, the centers were the first in the country to be accredited by the Joint Commission on Hospital Accreditation. But perhaps the greatest accolade paid the centers was the comment of a little old lady who said that "for the first time in my life, I believe someone really cares and is interested in me and my problems."

The same concern for the poor and minorities

was reflected inside the walls of the hospital where a new Department of Social Service under the direction of Miss Mildred Beard provided help and counseling to patients with particular emphasis on indigent patients. The hospital was also caring for an increasing number of charity cases and in some years the cost passed the $900,000 mark.

The neighborhood centers and the new social service department reflected Methodist's close ties to the Church, which were continually reaffirmed by the hospital Board and administration. Jack Hahn, in his 1961 report, commented on the opportunity in this "new era" for greater service by closer ties of the Church and hospital. Hahn wrote, "When Methodist Hospital was organized at the turn of the 20th century, it was in many ways a missionary project of the Church. It is today an even stronger outreach of Christianity in meeting Jesus' challenge 'to preach, to teach and to heal.'"

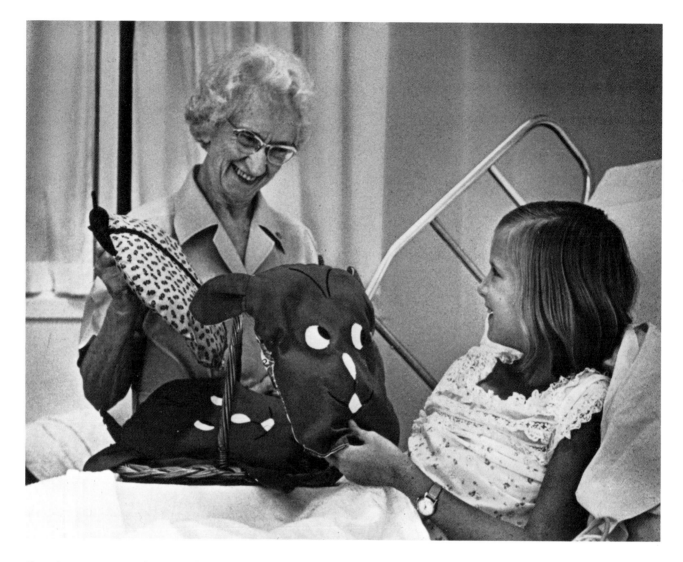

Since their organization during World War II, Pink Ladies of the White Cross Guild have been a part of the Methodist Hospital team. In this 1968 photo Pink Lady Helen Humphries presents a gift of a stuffed animal to 10-year old Jama Prange, a patient in the Children's Pavilion. Making stuffed animals for children is one of many Pink Lady activities. (Indianapolis News Photo, Patty Haley.)

The year 1968 marked the end of an era when, 60 years to the day, May 11, the Methodist Hospital School of Nursing graduated its last class of 77 students. The school had been phased out in favor of an associate of arts degree (two-year) in nursing by way of courses at the regional campus of Indiana University (now Indiana University-Purdue University at Indianapolis or IUPUI). The hospital, however, would continue its association with DePauw University and its four-year collegiate program. During its 60-year history, the Methodist school had achieved a proud record and graduated 3,668 nurses in its three-year programs. In closing the school, the Board of Trustees paid

special tribute to Miss Fredericka Koch, who had served as director of the school for the past 18 years.

For former graduates and faculty, there were memories to be cherished. Many would recall attending the welcoming tea as a nervous incoming student, the capping ceremonies marking the end of their probationary period, and the thrill of fastening the cross emblem to their left sleeves at the beginning of their junior year. And there were memories of the spring, fall and Christmas choral programs, attending Wednesday night chapel, and escorting patients to Sunday morning worship. In lighter moments there were Junior and Senior

Miss Fredericka Koch was Director of Nursing as well as Director of the Methodist Hospital School of Nursing until the 60-year old school was phased out in 1968. Miss Koch, who came to Indianapolis in 1950, was also the first director of the DePauw University School of Nursing. Before joining Methodist Hospital, Miss Koch held supervisory nursing positions at hospitals in Columbus and Youngstown, Ohio. "My 21 years at Methodist were the greatest," she said. "Methodist killed you with work, love and kindness."

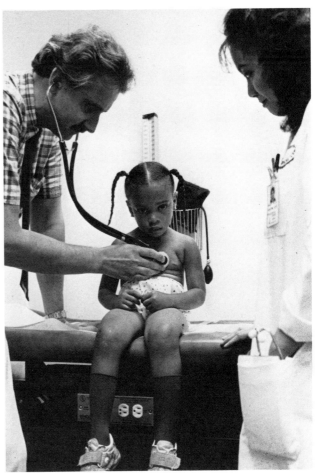

Drs. William Van Osdol (left) and Rosario N. Chau examine one of their younger patients at the Barrington Neighborhood Health Center.

Proms and Christmas trees to decorate and, oh what fun it was, to "borrow" the real skeleton used in the anatomy classes and scare the wits out of the "probies" or to hang "Mary Chase"—the realistic and lifelike dummy used in class—from a window in Wile Hall. But these were memories now. No longer would the walls ring with young voices lifted in the school song, "The Prayer Perfect" with words by the Hoosier poet, James Whitcomb Riley. Now the last class of the Methodist Hospital School of Nursing was gone and the classrooms were being converted to new uses. But visitors to the hospital would find a handsome reminder of the 77 young ladies who made up the 1968 graduating class—the comfortable furniture in the lob-

by of the newly completed front entrance was the class's gift to the hospital where they worked so hard and so long to become a member of a proud profession.

In keeping with the Wesleyan tradition, black men and women were playing a larger role in the operation of the hospital. More and more blacks were employed including many of the so-called "hard core" unemployed, who were given special help and training and asigned to jobs commensurate with their skills. In common with other employers, Methodist became an equal opportunity employer—a commitment it had made earlier in its history, but now required by law. Even more important, for the first time a black man, the Reverend Robert Smith, pastor of the Riverside Methodist Church, was elected to the Board of Trustees. He would later be joined by the Reverend N.H. Holloway, pastor of the Barnes Methodist

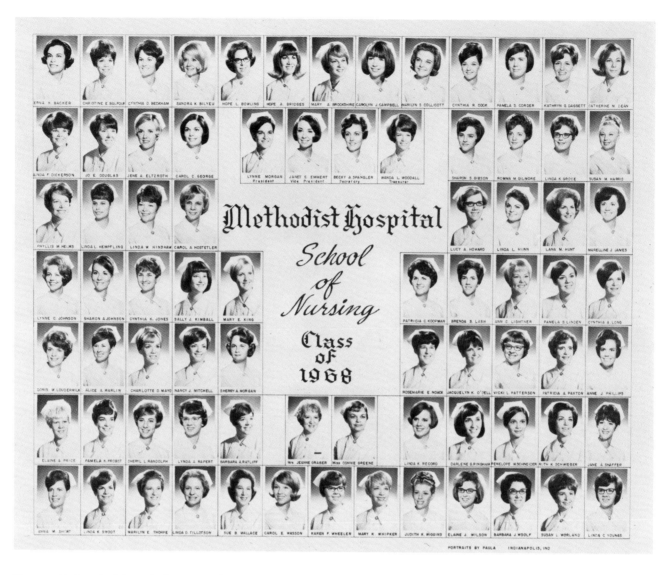

Methodist Hospital School of Nursing Class of 1968

PORTRAITS BY PAULA   INDIANAPOLIS, IND.

The year 1968 marked the end of an era as the Methodist Hospital School of Nursing graduated its last class consisting of 77 students. The 60-year old school was phased out in favor of an Associate of Arts degree (two year) in nursing by way of courses at the regional campus of Indiana University, now Indiana University-Purdue University at Indianapolis. The hospital also continued its association with DePauw University and its four year collegiate program. President of the '68 class was Lynne Morgan.

Church, and Sam Jones, executive director of the Indianapolis Chapter of the Urban League.

On April 23, 1968 an important and historic change took place in Methodism that would have an impact on the hospital as well as the Church—the joining of hands by Bishop Reuben H. Mueller of the Evangelical United Brethren Church and Bishop Lloyd C. Wicke of the Methodist Church symbolized the union of the two Wesleyan bodies into a United Methodist Church, a merger that had been contemplated since 1956. The five Indiana conferences of the churches now became the North and South Indiana Conferences and through their Divisions of Health and Welfare Ministries would continue to nominate the majority of trustees to the hospital board. Bishop Mueller, former president of the National Council of Churches, was appointed bishop of the Indiana Area and an ex-officio member of the Methodist Hospital Board of Trustees.

The pluralism of the new Church would provide minority groups—some racial, some national, and some social—with a greater voice and presence in the Methodist Church.

School Song, Methodist Hospital School of Nursing
Words by the Hoosier Poet, James Whitcomb Riley

The Prayer Perfect

Dear Lord! Kind Lord! Gracious Lord!
  I pray
Thou wilt look on all I love,
  Tenderly today!
Weed their hearts of weariness,
  Scatter ev'ry care
Down a wake of Angel wings
  Winnowing the air.
Bring unto the sorrowing
  All release from pain;
Let the lips of laughter
  Overflow again;
And with all the needy,
  O, divide I pray,
This vast treasure of content
  That is mine today!

Chapter Twelve

Proud and Shining Moments

For behold, I create new heavens and a new earth: . . . No more shall there be in it an infant that lives for a few days, or an old man who does not fill out his days, for the child shall die a hundred years old.
—Isaiah 65:17; 20-21a

Methodist Hospital wrote a dramatic new chapter in surgery on January 1, 1972 when it became the first hospital in Indiana to perform a kidney transplant operation and one of the first private hospitals in the nation to develop an organ transplant program.

The historic operation on a 29-year old Indianapolis woman was the culmination of planning and careful coordination by a multi-disciplinary team headed by Drs. LeRoy H. King, Jr. and Charles B. Carter, nephrologists recruited from the U.S. Army's renal dialysis program at Walter Reed Hospital. Other members of the team included Methodist staff physicians Drs. Phillip G. Mosbaugh and William E. Chapman, urologists; Drs. William S. Sobat and Gilbert Herod, surgeons; paramedical specialists; social service caseworkers; chaplains and financial consultants. The actual operation was performed by Methodist staff doctors and Drs. King and Carter, coordinators of the program, limited their efforts to thwarting the rejection process which frequently follows transplantation. They also functioned as pre-operative evaluators and post-operative patient managers. The program was supported by a substantial grant from the Indianapolis Foundation.

By 1977, the fifth year of the program, Methodist had performed 120 kidney transplants. More would have been performed but there was a continuing problem of obtaining sufficient kidneys from donors or cadavers and being able to match them with the patient. To assist in the procurement of viable kidneys, a full time kidney coordinator was appointed and a protocol developed. The coordinator, Lynn Driver, is on call 24 hours a day. With the assistance of Drs. Carter and King,

Life Line helicopter emergency service started in 1979 in response to the need to transport patients speedily in traumatic situations with a physician and nurse in attendance. Life Line plays an integral role in Methodist Hospital's Trauma Center — one of two in Indiana. In 1983, Life Line made 579 runs. The heliport provides a panoramic view of downtown Indianapolis. Chaplains use the heliport as a place to conduct Easter Sunrise worship services.

Air transport of human kidneys for transplant is now a common procedure. Methodist Hospital has operated a major kidney transplant program for 12 years. Shown here is Sharon Bowers, assistant transplant coordinator leaving a plane with a kidney for transplantation.

Driver established procurement programs in other Indiana cities and worked closely with physicians in establishing a cooperative program with Indiana University Medical Center and other transplant programs throughout the country. The Methodist transplant team and White Cross Guild joined in a scrap aluminum drive to purchase a specially equipped van for transport of cadaver organs from surrounding areas to Methodist Hospital. The van was equipped with a perfusion machine capable of preserving two kidneys up to 60 hours, the maximum time that a functioning kidney could be sustained.

One of the hospital's "perfect" kidney transplants was performed in November of 1979 when, in a four hour dual operation, Dr. William S. Sobat successfully transplanted a kidney from one identical twin to another. Earlier, the twin suffering from kidney failure, Randy Zorman, had rejected a kidney donated by his mother, Virginia. The second operation with his brother, Rick, donating a kidney, proved to be the successful

Sophisticated computers were enlisted in the war against disease and injury at Methodist Hospital in 1977. Shown here, the day the Methodist Hospital Information Computer System went into operation, are Zed Day, foreground, and Bob Nichols and Bob Cooney, far left.

The first physician to enter an order on Methodist Hospital's Computerized Medical Information System was Dr. Gilbert Herod. Looking on is Nurse Hazel Lawrence. The system became operational on September 20, 1977.

combination. Doctors said, among other things, the tissue match was "ideal." It was also the first kidney transplant performed on identical twins in Indiana.

The transplant program, as with many other Methodist innovative programs in medicine and surgery, was an outgrowth of planning and research conducted under the auspices of the hospital's Medical Research Department headed by Dr. Lloyd. In the case of the transplant program, it had logically developed from the research department's artificial kidney program which had been recognized since its beginning in 1966 for its excellence in patient care and training. In 1972 more than 60 patients participated in the home dialysis program and the number was growing.

In addition to its kidney transplant program, Methodist continued its leadership in open heart surgery. In 1971 some 300 of these intricate operations had been performed by Methodist staff physicians. For heart patients there was also on-site computer analysis of EKG data. Installed in 1978, the new mini-computer instantly analyzed cardiac information and produced an unconfirmed EKG report for physician interpretation and confirmation. Designed to receive heart data from an EKG machine by telephone transmission, the computer measured and recorded the patient's heart rhythm and rate and generated a printed analysis

for the physician's review. Once the doctor confirmed the report, Heart Station employees entered the information into the patient's medical records by way of the hospital's computerized Medical Information System.

Computerization of the hospital and the proliferation of new and more sophisticated equipment for the diagnosis and treatment of patients pushed equipment costs to over a million dollars a year, costs that were necessary for a prestigious hospital to maintain its standing commitment to excellence in health care. The new technology also made demands on hospital resources, dollars and space as well as requiring additional personnel. An example was the new computerized axial tomography equipment installed in 1974. The ninth to be installed in the United States, the CAT scanner as it was popularly known, combined the use of an X-ray with a computer to detect brain disorders. Its installation marked one more step in Methodist becoming a major center for the diagnosis of brain related problems. Two years later a new computerized tomography scanner was installed that would provide a scan of the patient's entire body using the same combination of X-ray and computer techniques.

The need for new equipment to stay abreast of rapidly advancing and sophisticated medical technology came at a time when wages and prices

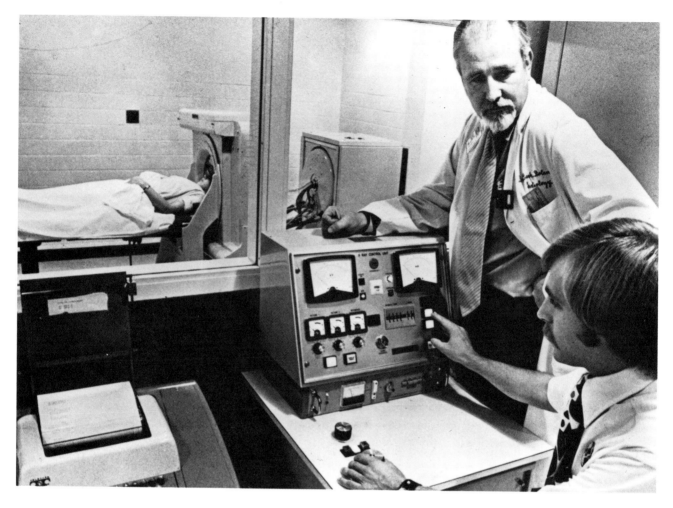

Installation of a $400,000 brain scanner in 1974 made it possible for doctors at Methodist Hospital to obtain a three-dimensional look into the human brain. The first to be installed in Indiana, the scanner provides a hundred times more useful information than conventional X-rays. Dr. Patrick Dolan (standing) director of radiology and Gerald Beckler initiated the new equipment. (Indianapolis News Photo, Tim Holcomb.)

were spiraling and the economy was well on its way to double digit inflation. Methodist, in common with other hospitals, was putting new economies into effect, but inflation continued to push up operating costs which in turn forced Methodist to regularly and reluctantly raise its room rates. The government's Economic Stabilization Program that froze wages, prices and rents brought a temporary halt in 1971, but when the freeze was lifted, hospital rates remained under the program. This proved a real hardship and at Methodist, already coping with slow payments from Medicare and third party payers and a resultant cash flow problem, it meant deficit financing during 1972.

While hospitals made every effort to keep their costs down and at the same time adhere to the principle that no one was to get less than the best of care, cost containment became a rallying cry for newspaper editors, consumer groups, magazine writers and some agencies of the federal government. Typical of the many newspaper articles of the period was a series of articles in *The Indianapolis Star*, the first headlined: "High Costs of Health Care Soaring Out of Sight—and Expected to Grow Worse."

No two men were more aware of the need for cost containment than Jack Hahn, president of Methodist Hospital (the new title of president was part of a corporate change in 1968) and Clyde Fields, vice-president, finance. Hahn was a nationally known authority on hospitals and their problems. He had served as president of the

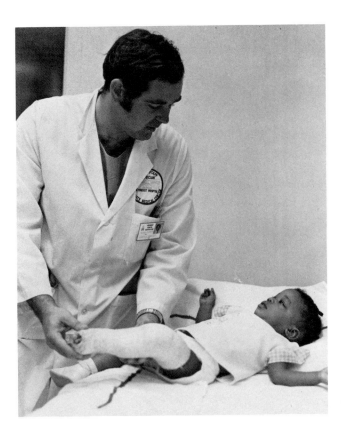

Outpatient visits in every category represent the most dramatic growth in service in the hospital's history in 1974. Here an orthopedic resident cares for a small child as part of his medical education. Treatment by a resident house staff physician under supervision of an attending physician faculty makes for the best possible medical care.

American Hospital Association as well as president of the American Protestant Hospital Association, the Indiana Hospital Association and the National Association of Methodist Health and Welfare Ministries. He was a former Commissioner of the Joint Commission on Accreditation of Hospitals from 1973-76, the first non-physician chairman in 1976 and chairman of the Committee on Research and Education, 1976-78. He was also a Fellow and Regent of the American College of Hospital Administrators and a consultant to the United States Surgeon General. Aided by a strong Board with a positive and progressive view, Hahn moved to effect new economies as well as maintain Methodist Hospital's leadership in providing the best in health care.

Under Hahn's leadership measures were adopted to reduce patient costs by reducing the length of hospitalization, making greater use of out-patient facilities and extending the volunteer programs of White Cross Guild, Pink Ladies and the Beaconettes, the latter made up of teenagers. Tighter inventory controls were established, linen conservation programs instituted, and a self-insured workmen's compensation program put into operation. To reduce sick leave and the costs of Methodist's health insurance program, employees were given a free health hazard appraisal. Energy costs were cut by using the hospital's standby generators for 16 hours a day. Contracts were renegotiated and long existing contracts put up for new competitive bids. Hahn would later praise Fields for his contributions in helping to control costs and improve the hospital's cash flow during this trying period. Also singled out for high praise was Bryan A. Rogers, executive vice-president, for his administrative leadership particularly during 1971.

Methodist was among the first health care providers to participate in "The Voluntary Effort to Contain Health Care Costs," a national program sponsored by the American Hospital Association, the American Medical Association and the Federation of American Hospitals. Local, state and national organizations joined in praising Methodist for its cost containment program and the rate review committee of the Indiana Hospital Association (IHA), after a thorough examination of Methodist's efficient and economical operation, authorized modest rate increases. (Jack Hahn had been one of three men who helped establish the rate review committee of IHA. The committee, which passes on all applications for contemplated rate increases, allows increases only when it is established that the hospital is operating at peak efficiency and a rate increase is deemed essential to operations.)

A Shared Services program was inaugurated in 1976 that once again demonstrated Methodist's concern and leadership in cost containment. The program with the avowed purpose of holding down hospital costs by eliminating unnecessary capital expenditures and costly duplication of services, provided special services to nearby and outlying hospitals including medical and diagnostic care, management skills and seminars. Two examples of the Shared Services program were the Heart Station monitoring of caridac patients in out-of-the-city hospitals and a mobile radiology van that took sophisticated and expensive X-ray equipment to small county hospitals on a regular basis. The Shared Services program, considerably expanded, remains in operation today.

The increasing role of the federal government was proving an added problem in terms of time and money. Medicare and Medicaid programs, which had been established by Congress in the 1960s, added a new second party payer as well as a new layer of bureaucracy. Controversies developed over charges and delays in payment were frequent and affected hospitals' cash flow. The Central Indiana Health Systems Agency, a government subsidized and consumer dominated agency, provided yet another delay to hospital development. All expansion plans had to be approved by sub-area councils and the approvals or disapprovals

then moved through the agency's board, the State Health Agency and finally to the Secretary of Health, Education and Welfare. A project moving through the four bureaucratic tiers could delay needed projects for months and, in a time of rapidly increasing inflation, push up original costs. In addition, the Health Systems Agency was authorized to approve all hospital expenditures of $100,000 or more for equipment. (The Agency, whose budget approximated $1,000,000 was finally phased out during the Reagan administration although the State Agency continues to function and pass on hospital plans and capital expenditures.)

Perhaps the best comment on cost containment

Since its beginning, Methodist Hospital has carried out a continuing program of medical staff education. Typical was the visit of Dr. Paul Dudley White, internationally known cardiologist, shown here. Others in the photograph are, standing (l. to r.) Dr. Robert D. Pickett,

Dr. Lester D. Bibler and Dr. Jack H. Hall, vice president Medical Education. Seated are Dr. William D. Gambill, Dr. White and, at far right, Dr. Harvey Middleton, all members of the Hospital staff.

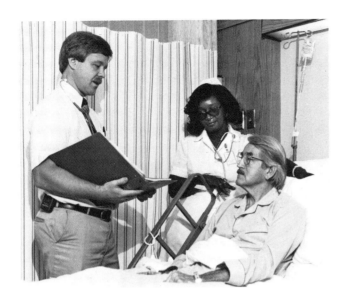

The interrelationship between a patient's faith, attitude and effective medical treatment has been known for a long time and is greatly respected by physicians and staff of Methodist Hospital. Above, a house staff physician and nurse conduct a patient satisfaction interview with a patient.

The 12-story Medical Tower was completed in 1975 by a group of private investors to serve physicians, patients of Methodist Hospital and their families. It housed offices for 100 physicians, a 110 bed hotel, a ground-floor restaurant, bank, gift shop, drug store and other facilities. Methodist purchased the third floor and moved the heart station, nuclear radiology, audiology and speech pathology departments and the Family Practice Center to the new building.

was incorporated in President Hahn's 1978 annual report to the Board of Trustees. Pointing out that Methodist was doing its utmost to cut costs, he wrote: "There is no such thing as inexpensive quality. When one's life is at stake, one wants the best. Second best is unacceptable. Methodist Hospital will continue to provide the best care possible."

In contrast with the 1960s, which saw more changes in the hospital's facilities than in any other decade, the 1970s brought few new buildings but renewed emphasis on renovating and remodeling older buildings. Wile and Wesley Halls, no longer needed for student housing, were filled with offices and ancillary departments and in 1978 Wesley Hall was demolished. Wile Hall was given a face lift including a new front entrance, ramps, and a tunnel connecting it with the garage. More land became available in the vicinity of the hospital and the Board of Trustees authorized its purchase for further expansion. The so-called "Castle Building" at the corner of 16th Street and Senate was purchased and demolished. A building at 1500 Stadium Drive was acquired and its 67,000 square feet of space given over to warehousing, print shop and financial services.

The Hospital joined with the Near Northside Development Association, a group of business and community leaders, in making plans for preserving and improving the area surrounding the hospital. Alex L. Taggart, III, president of the association, was a former chairman of the hospital Board. The possibility of moving Methodist Hospital from the inner city was studied, discussed and a decision made to remain in the present location—a decision re-affirmed in 1970. Board members cited Methodist's commitment to the inner city, moving and building costs, the planned revitalization of downtown and surrounding areas and the accessibility of the hospital from all areas of the city and outlying areas, an important factor for a hospital that functioned as a major referral center.

A new $600,000 Memorial Pavilion was built on the fifth floor of the South Building in 1977 and connected to the Krannert Tower to provide eight additional private rooms and one suite. An expansion of the luxury accommodations on the Krannert fifth floor, the pavilion's cost was funded in part from a $2,200,000 gift received in 1975 from anonymous donors.

Across the street from Methodist, on Capitol Avenue, a new 12-story, $10,000,000 building, the Medical Tower, was completed in 1975. The dream of Dr. John R. Melin and built by a group of

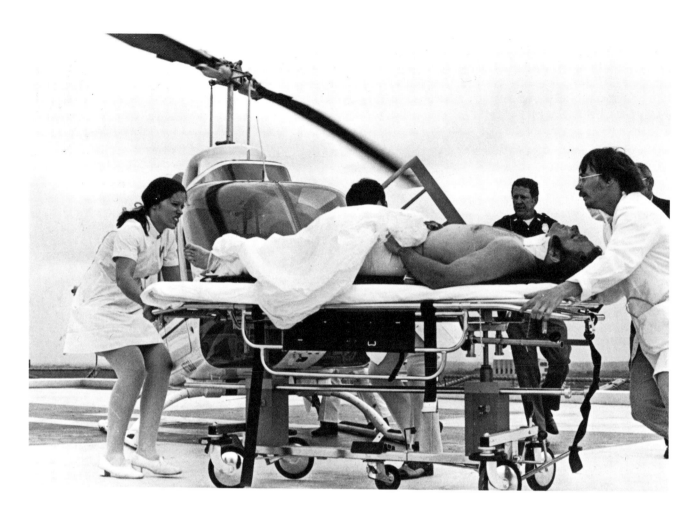

Methodist Hospital's famous "Life Line" in action. A doctor and nurse rush a patient from helicopter to an emergency operating room in this 1979 photograph. In the 1980s, Life Line speeds a physician, nurse and emergency equipment to accident scenes and hospitals in central Indiana nearly 600 times a year.

private investors, including the doctor, the Tower housed offices for some 100 physicians, a 110-room hotel and a ground floor restaurant, bank, gift shop, drug store and other facilities. Methodist purchased the third floor of the building which was connected to the hospital's A-building by a climate controlled, steel and glass skywalk over Capitol Avenue. Methodist's Heart Station, Nuclear Radiology, Audiology and Speech Pathology Departments and the Family Practice Center were moved to the new building.

Recognizing the need for better and faster ways to bring emergency medical care to the critically ill and injured, Methodist Hospital began experimenting with helicopter emergency service in 1970. The helicopter was initially used to speed patients from the Speedway Emergency Hospital to a

Methodist parking lot. In July of 1979 the airborne emergency service, now known as "Life Line," became a full fledged and important part of the hospital's emergency care and trauma center with the lease of a 206L-1 Ranger II Helicopter combined with the earlier installation of a modern heliport on the roof of the new Capitol Avenue addition. Capable of flying within a 150 mile radius of Indianapolis, the service could speed emergency equipment and a doctor and nurse trained in emergency medicine to the injured and ill at speeds of 130 miles per hour. A year later, a more advanced helicopter, a 105 CBS went into service, the first twin engine helicopter to be used in a medical setting in the United States. Today "Life Line" speeds a physician, nurse and emergency equipment to accidents and hospitals 570 times a year.

Methodist's concern for the inner city and its problems resulted in the opening of a third neighborhood health center on the southwest side in addition to the Central Avenue and Southeast Centers. The hospital's initiative "for providing health care to the poor and minority groups," was cited

Mrs. Ralph W. (Grace) Showalter willed $2 million dollars to develop a cardiac treatment fund. She died July 23, 1972. A cardiovascular care unit was established and endowed by this fund. Board chairman, Russell R. Hirschman said, "Everyone associated with Methodist Hospital is deeply appreciative of this generous gift, which is the largest restricted endowment ever received by the hospital."

The Hall of Fame in Philanthropy of the United Methodist Health and Welfare Ministries has elected five benefactors of Methodist Hospital to its illustrious membership for their philanthropic deeds: Mr. Edward F. Gallahue, 1955, the first Hoosier to receive this honor; Mr. and Mrs. Herman C. Krannert, 1966; Mr. Francis M. Hughes, 1969; Mr. and Mrs. Nicholas H. Noyes, 1970; and Dr. Richard M. Nay, 1978.

by the Board of Global Ministries of the United Methodist Church at its 1974 convention.

A Drug Abuse Center, which proved to be a model of its kind, was established at 30th and Clifton Streets and funded by the National Institute of Mental Health through the Community Addiction Services Agency (CASA). A Center for Alcohol Abuse, operating under the aegis of the Family Practice Center, was opened in 1972 under the direction of Dr. Catherine J. Connelly. Funded by Lilly Endowment with an additional drinking and driving grant from the Department of Transportation, City of Indianapolis, the center provided 674 treatments in its first year, and by 1974 the number had increased to 9,391.

Largely through the efforts of Dr. Richard Nay of the Methodist Medical Staff, Mrs. Grace Showalter, widow of Ralph Showalter, former export director of Eli Lilly and Company, established the Showalter Cardiac Treatment Fund of $2,000,000. The fund enabled the hospital to purchase equipment necessary for sophisticated surgery and cardiovascular care and the evaluation of cardiac progress.

A major achievement of the 1970s was an increase in the services for the care of the critically ill or injured. In 1976, for example, the hospital had 140 beds classified as intensive care beds: Intensive Care, Coronary Care, Open Heart Recovery, Special Care Nursery, Pediatric Intensive Care,

Dr. William Niles Wishard, Jr. of the Methodist Hospital medical staff and a nationally known urologist, was the 1973 recipient of the prestigious Ramon Guiteras Award of the American Urological Society. Dr. Wishard, who died shortly after receiving the award, was a past president of the medical staff and a member of the board of directors of the Methodist Hospital Foundation.

President and Chief Executive Officer Jack A. L. Hahn, known for his "open door" policy for all employees, making early morning rounds of the hospital, insistence on starting and ending meetings on time, and ability to know employees by first name, enjoyed the respect and loyalty of employees at all levels in the hospital.

Neuro Constant Care, Spinal Cord, Chronic Renal and Medical Research.

A Clinical Oncology Center was established in 1975 with funds from the National Cancer Institute to develop a "model of care" for community hospital cancer programs. Dr. William M. Dugan, Jr. was named director. The Center also conducted clinical research on pain medication, diagnostic and therapeutic radiology and tumor registry. In 1979 Methodist counted 2,634 primary and recurrent cancer admissions. Three National Seminars on Community Cancer Care—1979, 1981, 1983— were sponsored by the Center and a fourth one is planned for 1985. A move in oncology, as in other branches of medicine, is toward prevention, detection and early treatment.

Methodist was also a midwest referral center for patients from out of the city and state suffering from head, neck injuries and neurological problems. The hospital's Neuroscience Center performed 200 major brain operations and hundreds of spinal procedures yearly. The neuroscience area included a 44-bed neurosurgical care unit, a 10-bed neuro-constant care unit and an 11-bed Indiana Regional Spinal Cord Center, under the direction of Dr. Robert K. Silbert.

New at the hospital in 1973 was a Speech and Hearing Therapy program designed to provide a more complete service to long term patients and aid physicians in diagnosis and evaluation. Special beneficiaries of the program were young patients with speech and hearing problems and adults suffering brain damage from strokes and accidents. Initial funds for the program were provided by the First Annual Mohawk Hills Golf Classic.

It was during the 1970s that Methodist Hospital and the Indiana University School of Medicine signed an agreement providing for "a well organized cooperative program of medical education involving an affiliation with the School of Medicine." Methodist and the School of Medicine had had informal ties from the beginning through faculty members who practiced medicine at Methodist and participated in its Continuing and Graduate Medical Education programs. The signing of the agreement on October 16, 1970, was, in a sense, a formalization of a long time relationship. Under the terms of the agreement the Hospital and the School retained their independent status, but spelled out procedures and policies, clarified financing and grant applications, and provided for an exchange of faculty.

Since its beginnings in 1908, the medical staff at Methodist Hospital had been recognized as one of the best in Indiana and many members were nationally and internationally known for their achievements in medicine or surgery. Among these was Dr. William Niles Wishard, Jr., one of the

nation's foremost urologists, who, in 1973, was awarded the most prestigous award of the American Urological Society—the Ramon Guiteras Award. A long time member of the Methodist medical staff, Dr. Wishard served as a member of the Board of Directors of the Methodist Hospital Foundation, of the Medical Staff and chairman of the Professional Standards, Research and Joint Liaison Committee. A graduate of Harvard Medical School, Dr. Wishard was the third generation of physicians in his family who had practiced medicine continuously since Indiana's statehood in 1816. Dr. Wishard, who died soon after receiving the Guiteras Award, is remembered today with a handsome memorial plaque, donated by the urology service and unveiled at Methodist Hospital in April, 1975.

For Jack Hahn, president and chief executive officer of Methodist, came a new award—the Distinguished Service Award of the American Hospital Association. In announcing Hahn as the recipient of the award, John Alexander McMahon, AHA president, said: "Mr. Hahn is a leader of the greatest magnitude in the hospital field and one that the association is justly proud to honor with this award, the highest it can bestow."

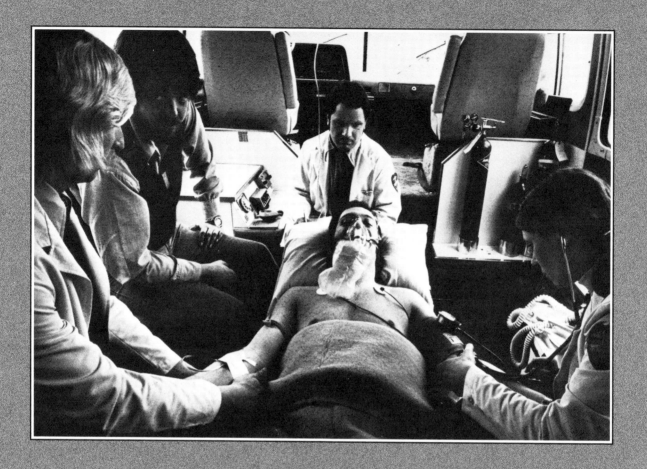

Chapter Thirteen

Looking Back, Moving Forward

"The interrelationship between faith and attitude of the patient and the effect of physical intervention is one of the oldest, most consistently overlooked, and constantly rediscovered pieces of medical knowledge."
—*The Mechanic and the Gardener*
Lawrence LeShan
1982

Paramedics to the rescue. In this simulated exercise, highly trained paramedics, members of Ambulance Indianapolis Dispatch (AID) are preparing a heart attack victim for transport to Methodist Hospital. Shown in the photo are (second from left) Bill Arthur, Methodist's clinical instructor and AID paramedics Gary Lentz (lower left) and Ron Gilbert and Kathy Shackelford at right. The "patient" is Harry Watson, also an AID paramedic.

Methodist Hospital celebrated its 75th anniversary in 1974 with a year-long program of events designed to create greater public awareness of Methodist's goals and objectives and its human and physical resources. There was much to be proud of in the hospital's diamond jubilee year for the hospital boasted a record of growth and progress that could be matched by few hospitals. From a small 65-bed hospital, it now had facilities to care for 1105 patients, a medical staff of 750 physicians and surgeons, 3,500 employees and more than 2,000 volunteers. Its buildings and grounds covered some 29 acres and its annual budget was in the area of $50,000,000. And, in keeping with Christian principles and traditions, Methodist annually provided some $2,000,000 in charity service.

A hospital, however, is more than bricks and mortar and perhaps this was best summed up in the 75th anniversary theme which grew out of a hospital-wide employee contest. The winning theme, submitted by Clarence Johnson, instrumentation supervisor in the laboratory, reflected the hospital's approach to healing: "Compassionate Health Care: Our Mission for 75 Years—STILL IS!" The theme was incorporated in all printed material and widely publicized throughout the anniversary year. Members of the anniversary celebration committee were: Eldon Campbell, chairman; Mrs. Ruby Schahet; Dr. Louis W. Nie; Mrs. Robert Perkins; Lester Irons; and Robert Suckow, director of development and public relations. Jack Hahn was an ex-officio committee member.

The anniversary year began with proclamations from Governor Otis Bowen, M.D. and Mayor Richard Lugar proclaiming 1974 as a "Year of

Testifying to the Congressional Hearing is Dr. Hugh K. Thatcher, left, President of Methodist Hospital Medical Staff, and Dr. James H. Gosman, immediate past president of the Indiana State Medical Association.

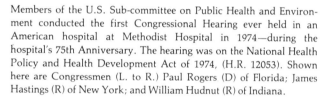

Members of the U.S. Sub-committee on Public Health and Environment conducted the first Congressional Hearing ever held in an American hospital at Methodist Hospital in 1974—during the hospital's 75th Anniversary. The hearing was on the National Health Policy and Health Development Act of 1974, (H.R. 12053). Shown here are Congressmen (L. to R.) Paul Rogers (D) of Florida; James Hastings (R) of New York; and William Hudnut (R) of Indiana.

Recognition for Methodist Hospital of Indiana." Highlights of the months that followed included the annual White Cross Guild luncheon, the triennial homecoming for the old school of nursing, a health careers program, a religion and health symposium and, in March, the first Congressional hearing ever held in an American Hospital. The hearings, conducted by the Public Health and Environment Sub-committee of the United States House of Representatives, were held in the White Cross Service Center and were highlighted by testimony from local health leaders on the proposed National Health Policy and Development Act of 1974. Then congressman, later Mayor William H. Hudnut III was a member of the committee. Methodist was chosen as the site for the hearings in view of its major local and national role in health care.

The anniversary celebration was climaxed by a 75th anniversary dinner attended by 800 people at the Indiana Convention Exposition Center on November 12, 1974. The principal speakers were Oscar Robertson, a graduate of Crispus Attucks High School and for three years the Most Valuable

Player in the National Basketball Association; and Dr. Morris Fishbein, editor of *Medical World News*, a former Indiana resident and an unofficial spokesman for American medicine. Both Robertson and Dr. Fishbein were born and graduated from high school in the Methodist Hospital neighborhood. Mr. Campbell presided and other speakers included Mayor Lugar; Francis M. Hughes, president of the Methodist Hospital Foundation; Governor Otis T. Bowen, Indiana governor; Jack Hahn, hospital president; Lester Irons, chairman of the hospital Board of Trustees; and Dr. Hugh K. Thatcher, Jr., president of the medical staff. The invocation and benediction were given by Bishop John P. Craine of the Indianapolis Episcopal Diocese and the Reverend N.H. Holloway, pastor of the Barnes United Methodist Church, both members of the hospital Board.

In 1974, the same year Methodist celebrated its 75th anniversary, the hospital established the first Emergency Medical Services Training Center and introduced a new word into the lexicon of health care in Indiana—paramedic. The first paramedic class, consisting entirely of Ambulance Indianapolis Dispatch (AID) employees, entered the hospital in January for a nine-month, 1,000-hour course under the direction of William Arthur. At the conclusion of the intensive and rigorous course, Methodist's first clinical affiliate, AID, Inc., became operational. As news spread of the center and its valuable training, requests poured in to provide classes for other health care and

The Medical Staff, during the 75th Anniversary, developed a program to honor physicians of fifty years' membership. Shown here are: Dr. Hugh K. Thatcher, President of the Medical Staff; Dr. J.O. Ritchey; Dr. Goethe Link; Dr. J.K. Berman and Dr. Roy Lee Smith. Missing is Dr. Rollin H. Moser.

emergency groups around the state.

Aided by federal grants and other funding, the EMS program grew and expanded. In-house training was extended to provide orientation and special training in new emergency techniques for hospital nurses in emergency departments. Under David Vance, who succeeded Arthur in 1977, Methodist's EMS program became the first to require cardiac life support as a prerequisite for graduation and affiliation. The center also established the first audit and review program for graduates, the first continuing education program and the first in-flight nurse training. By the late 1970s emergency medical training was established on a statewide basis. In the 1980s Methodist's EMS courses provided for a feeder system to over 30 ambulance services and 16 providers in Indiana.

The paramedic program was among the 40 teaching programs underway at Methodist. Others included a respiratory therapy technician program started in the summer of 1974 with an affiliation agreement with Butler University. In 1979 the program expanded to include not only a technician certificate program, but an associate degree therapist program. In 1981 the program was transferred administratively from the Respiratory Therapy Department to the newly created H. Walton Connelly, Jr. Allied Health Education Center in Academic Affairs. Dr. Connelly, a former vice president for human resources, was a long time member of the staff and a much beloved personality until his sudden death in January, 1981.

Among other highly acclaimed Methodist teaching programs was the Nursing and Allied Health Continuing Education program established in 1975 through the efforts of Ruth Parke, director of nursing; John Mote, vice president, administration; Dr. H. Walton Connelly, director of education and training; and Jean Haehl, director of staff development. Designed to provide continuing education for licensed and certified personnel of the hospital, the first workshop was presented on November 5, 1975 under the direction of Dr. Sharon Isaac, coordinator. Dr. Isaac was instrumental in developing the philosophy, goals and procedures for implementing continuing education offerings. The special value of the program was its emphasis on the ever increasing technological advances in the health care field. Recognizing the need to include out-of-the-city participants, the program expanded and grew. In the next eight years more than 200 workshops were

Dr. Otis R. Bowen, governor of Indiana; Dr. Jack A.L. Hahn, president of Methodist Hospital; and Dr. Morris Fishbein share a laugh during the hospital's 75th Anniversary celebration at the convention Center on November 12, 1974. Dr. Fishbein, a 1906 graduate of Shortridge High School, remembered the actual construction of Methodist Hospital. He was editor of the *Journal of the American Medical Association* for 26 years and was unofficial spokesman for American medicine for two generations.

presented, attended by nurses and certified personnel from all over Indiana as well as seven other states. In 1978, Methodist Hospital became the first hospital to receive a two-year accreditation from the Indiana State Nurses Association Committee on Accreditation.

Methodist's strong commitment to nursing and the quality of health care was reaffirmed in 1978 with the appointment of Susan Sheedy, R.N., M.S., as the hospital's first vice-president for nursing.

A shortage of nurses persisted throughout the 1970s as it had in the preceding decades and Mrs.

Sheedy was active in a new Methodist program to recruit additional nurses. Among the steps taken were bonuses for employees who referred nurses to Methodist for employment and the development of a successful hospital based pool for temporary nursing help. Methodist nurses also traveled to colleges, universities and health care conventions to recruit young men and women for the staff. As time went on, the shortage eased, but it would persist into the 1980s.

There was yet another first for Methodist with the establishment of a hospice program for terminally ill patients. The program grew out of the

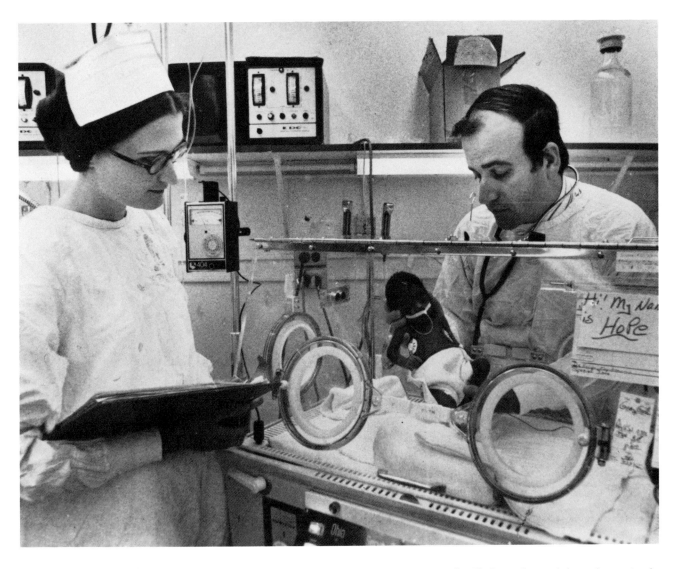

The special care nursery contained the first life-support ceiling in the United States. Dr. Richard Baum was the state's first director of neonatal pediatrics. Here he is seen with Kathy Visovatti, R.N. examining a newborn. In the 1970s the nursery cared for over 250 newborn babies annually. The lives of many babies who previously would have died are now saved. (Indianapolis Star Photo)

concerns of William C. Elliott, M.D., chairman of the Intensive Care Unit Committee of the medical staff, who was joined by others who shared his concern, including nurses, chaplains and educators. Objective of the program was to bring pain and symptoms under control so patients could spend their remaining days at home or, as an alternative, spend their last days at the hospital in pleasant, home like surroundings with the best of care including skilled nursing, family support, and spiritual counseling. The 11-bed unit on 5A, under the direction of Judith A. Barrett,R.N., associate director of medical research, operated on an ex-perimental basis during 1977. It was moved to 8-C the following year and became the first hospital based hospice in the United States. The program continues today as an integral part of the hospital.

In common with other hospitals, Methodist faced an important policy decision in 1973 when the United States Supreme Court handed down a landmark ruling declaring unconstitutional all state laws that prohibited voluntary abortions before the third month of pregnancy and established limits on abortion during the second three months. The city's Catholic hospitals immediately reaffirmed their policy of no abortions within their

Ten years of community service. U.S. Senator Richard G. Lugar cut a ribbon on October 24, 1978 marking the opening of Methodist Hospital's Neighborhood Health Centers' 10th anniversary celebration. Taking part in the ribbon cutting ceremony were: (l. to r.) Tom Strain, assistant director of the Centers; Dr. Dale S. Benson, NHC director; Senator Lugar, Lillian Stevenson, R.N., and Roger Coleman, director of Neighborhood Services for the City of Indianapolis.

Hospice is a program of care that combines technology and tenderness in a home-like atmosphere where the patient can be comfortable with family and friends to make the road less rocky and lonely. Methodist Hospital's Hospice Program was the first in a general hospital in the United States when it started in 1977.

walls and many city doctors, interviewed by the local newspapers, stated flatly they would not perform abortions.

Methodist Hospital, after much discussion, reaffirmed its policy. It would permit termination of a pregnancy, provided the patient's physician showed medical reason for terminating the pregnancy and the patient has benefit of counseling offered by a social service agency, the pastoral counseling service, a psychologist or psychiatrist, or a minister.

On the other hand, Methodist, which throughout its history had been dedicated to reducing infant mortality, took another important step in 1973 with the opening of a "totally revamped" Special Care Unit and Newborn Center under the direction of Dr. Richard Baum, the state's first director of neonatal pediatrics. The Special Care Nursery with 27 bassinets for prematurely born and high risk infants incorporated special equipment used for the first time in a United States hospital—a life support ceiling that furnished oxygen, compressed air, electric power and suction.

In its first year the special unit cared for 658 neonatals including 59 infants from all parts of the state. As a result of increasing demands from other hospitals, highly skilled doctor-nurse transport teams were developed. A Newborn Hotline (dial

NEW-BORN) consultation service was installed. Indicative of Methodist's leadership in caring for the newborn was a symposium on "Major Dilemmas in Neonatal Pediatrics" that drew an attendance of over 200 including 120 from outside the city. This concern combined with the interest of Drs. John R. Melin and Ray Antley brought about an introduction of medical genetics into the practice of obstetrics at Methodist Hospital.

Medical Research under Dr. Lloyd, continued as one of the hospital's most important and prestigious departments. During the 1970s 30 or more projects a year were researched with a budget that often passed the $2,000,000 mark, much of it from grants, gifts and endowments. Among many successful projects was the use of surgical bone cement for the replacement of fingers, elbows and hip bones. Grants from the Central Indiana Chapter of the National Cystic Fibrosis Research Foundation financed the establishment and maintenance of a Chronic Pulmonary Disease Clinic specifically designed for patients suffering from the disease. Additional

Active community leader and recipient of many community service awards, Chairman of the Board Eldon Campbell provided leadership and counsel in initiating the studies that eventuated in the hospital's reorganization and planning process looking ahead to the 21st century.

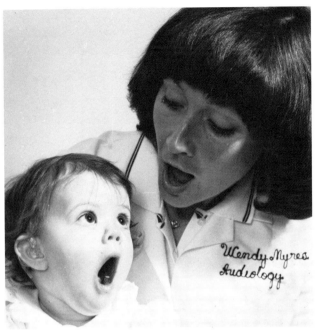

Wendy Myres, Methodist Hospital audiologist, works with Mindy Schmidt in the hospital's audiology department.

donations from the National Cystic Fibrosis Foundation and other organizations provided financing in succeeding years under the direction of Dr. Gabriel Rosenberg, director of pediatric medical education.

Following a review of Methodist Hospital's operations with Jack Hahn in 1976, Eldon Campbell, chairman of the Board, appointed a long range planning committee to re-examine the hospital's corporate mission, goals and future directions. The revised mission statement, which represented only minor modification of the hospital's original articles of incorporation in 1899, declared:

"The purposes of Methodist Hospital of Indiana, Inc., are to establish and maintain hospitals for the treatment of the sick, wounded and injured persons without respect to creed, color or nationality; to dispense relief and charity to the poor and destitute; to provide educational opportunities for allied health personnel, clergymen and volunteers and to cooperate with other formal educational programs conducted totally or in part on the Methodist Hospital campus; to conduct scientific research in the fields of medicine and hospitalization; and to give opportunity for students of medicine and members of the hospital medical staffs to acquire further practical knowledge of the art and science of medicine."

The statement established the following seven corporate goals which would provide a direction for the hospital in the next five years:

1. Operate health care facilities to provide a wholistic, comprehensive range of health care services. Emphasis will be placed on continued growth as a tertiary referral hospital serving primarily Marion County and the seven contiguous counties, and, for some services, the entire state. The hospital will also continue to provide pri-

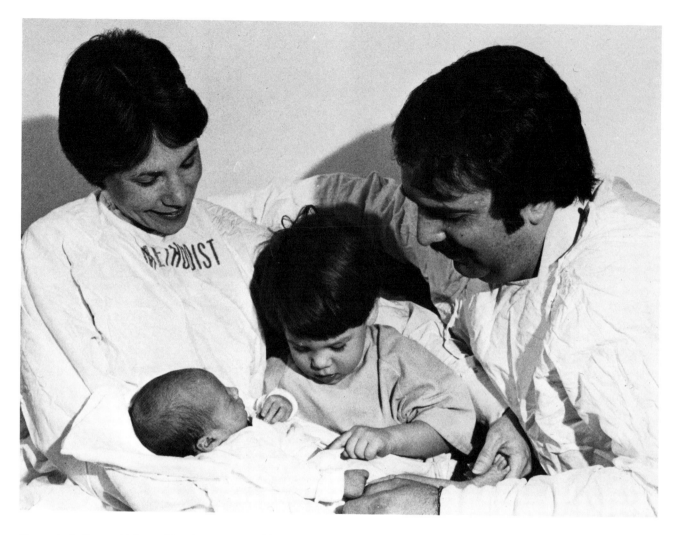

Two-and-a-half year old Steven Humphrey gets a good look at baby brother, Jacob, in the nursery at Methodist Hospital while parents Michael and Sandy share in the meeting. Sibling visitation began years ago; now older brothers and sisters are allowed to touch and hold their new babies. "Hands-on" sibling visitation is allowed by appointment only and not on the day of delivery.

mary care services as appropriate. Services provided will meet the psychological and social needs of patients as well as physical needs.

2. Continue to serve in a leadership role in the planning and community health services in cooperation with other institutional and health agencies. Continuity of care will be fostered through liaison with other providers. New programs to fulfill health needs of the community will be developed by the institution only after careful evaluation.

3. Provide a broad range of outreach services including community education, shared services and satellite facilities.

4. Provide educational programs for physicians, allied health personnel, chaplains, other employees and volunteers as needed, either directly or through cooperative arrangements.

5. Conduct research related to its developing specialized services and reflective of the needs of the attending and house staffs.

6. Fulfill the responsibilities of good corporate citizenship by remaining in its present location and working cooperatively with area businesses, organizations and residents to improve the hospital vicinity.

7. Maintain a sound financial structure, good employee practices and adherence to Christian principles.

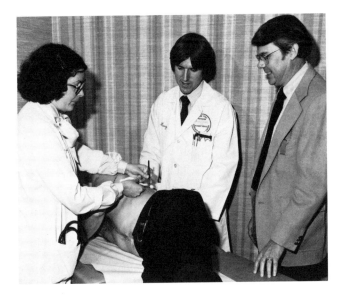

The Center for Surgical Sciences and Trauma is a newly constructed surgery clinic complete with a classroom, surgical library and endoscopic laboratory. The Center is designed to allow residents the opportunity to see patients in an atmosphere closely resembling a private practice situation. Here, an attending physician faculty member, Dr. A. Cedric Johnson, Jr., supervises an outpatient surgical procedure being performed by Drs. Martha Snyder and Brian Haag.

Mary Salmon, physical therapist, supervises a patient in Methodist Hospital's Rehabilitation Unit. The unit is one more example of the hospital's role as a complete health care provider.

Continuing Medical Education

Continuing Medical Education (CME) for staff physicians has been a mission of Methodist Hospital since it was established in 1899 as a charitable and educational organization. One of its goals is to provide "opportunities for students of medicine and members of the hospital medical staff to acquire further practical knowledge in the art and science of medicine." Ultimately, continuing medical education improves health care services by enabling participating physicians to obtain additional knowledge and skills, and to further develop professional performances and clinical judgment. The CME program is organized to plan, develop, implement and evaluate a wide range of educational activities based on the needs of the medical staff. Educational activities include: specialty or sub-specialty conferences; e.g., pediatric critical care and gynecologic urology symposiums; conferences to present transfer of new technological information; e.g., cardiac transplant and lithotripter; grand rounds—weekly—teaching conferences in ten services; didactic teaching conferences; discussion clubs; publications and annual conferences on moral and ethical issues in medicine.

Several deceased and prominent staff physicians are honored through annual lectures—some endowed; e.g., the William N. Wishard lecture in urology, Gordon Batman lecture in orthopedics, J.O. Ritchey lecture in internal medicine, Harold C. Ochsner lecture in radiology, J.K. Berman lecture in surgery, and William A. Karsall lecture in obstetrics and gynecology.

The blending of advanced medical technology and human tenderness is achieved through joint commitment and collaboration of the medical staff, administration and hospital Board as reflected in the continuing medical education program.

Arnold Doub, (left), who as an 11-year-old boy attended the Epworth League convention which led to the founding of Methodist Hospital, and Jack A. L. Hahn, hospital superintendent, examine an original program book from the 1899 convention. The program book was found by a hospital volunteer who was sorting out some of her mother's possessions.

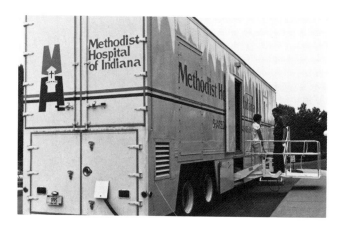

As part of a Shared Services program designed to eliminate unnecessary capital expenditures and costly duplication of services, Methodist Hospital equipped this van with a computerized axial tomography, CAT scanner, which visits nearby and outlying hospitals. In the photo above X-ray Technician Don Sullivan escorts Frances Cross down the ramp following her CAT scan at University Heights Hospital. The mobile unit can also accommodate wheelchairs and carts.

Methodist Hospital's employee, Miss Thelma Hawthorne, retired January 1, 1971 after 45 years and seven months of service — an all time record for length of service. Miss Hawthorne served as secretary to six hospital administrators, assistant secretary to the Board of Trustees, membership secretary of the White Cross Guild and secretary to the Medical Staff. After retirement she continued as secretary to the medical staff for a total of 52 years service.

Methodist had always been proud of its loyal and dedicated employees and on Tenure Nights (known as Tribute Time), nights set aside for a tribute to those with long years of service, there were always several employees with more than 25 years of service. However, the hospital experienced difficulty in keeping pace with changing times as reflected in personnel policies, employee benefits and management practices. This resulted in several attempts to organize the employees by different labor unions. The International Printing and Graphics Communication Union, Local 17, was sufficiently successful that the National Labor Relations Board ordered a vote in May, 1980. This and all other efforts were resisted by the employees which reflected the success of management in improving the employee relations climate through upgrading personnel policies, employee benefits and management practices.

Methodist's oldest employee in years of service was Thelma Hawthorne, who retired on January 1, 1971 after 45 years and seven months with the hospital—an all time record for length of service. *The Indianapolis Star* perhaps best summed up her years of service in an editorial on New Year's Day:

"Thelma Hawthorne has served as secretary—"right hand"—to six administrators, assistant secretary to the board of trustees, membership secretary of the White Cross Guild, and secretary to the medical staff. It has been a labor of love and loyalty and at Methodist the feeling has been mutual. As of today (January 1) she begins her official retirement. Since the habits of 46 years tend to persist, she will remain medical staff secretary on a part-time basis. The *Star* is happy to join the many well wishers congratulating this devoted lady whose dedicated hours, year by year, were the beat of the heart of a hospital."

There was also praise from the Board of Trustees in the form of a resolution and an editorial by Jack Hahn in *The Beacon*. As for Miss Hawthorne, she continued as secretary to the medical staff until shortly before her death in May, 1978—a record of 52 years of service to the hospital she loved and to which she had dedicated her life.

Chapter Fourteen

Plans for a New Century

The early years of the new decade brought a reorganization and restructuring of Methodist Hospital and the launching of the hospital's largest and most ambitious construction program—a $152,000,000 program designed to take Methodist into the 21st century.

The reorganizing and restructuring as well as the building program upon which it was predicated, were the result of intensive studies conducted by professional consultants and an in-depth study by the Board of Trustees' Planning Committee headed by Willaim G. Davis, Jr., a vice president of Eli Lilly and Company.

One of the results of the reorganization was a change at the top. On April 1, 1981, Jack A.L. Hahn, who had served as hospital superintendent and president for nearly 29 years—more than double the years of any predecessor—stepped aside to take a newly created post, chairman of the hospital. In August, however, Hahn announced he had "requested and been granted a phasing in of my retirement program and relief from on-going administrative authority and responsibility."

The new president and chief executive officer of Methodist Hospital was Dr. Frank P. Lloyd, a member of the hospital's executive committee and for many years vice president of Methodist's Medical Research Department, where his dynamic leadership had often put Methodist in the forefront of new medical achievements. Dr. Lloyd, however, brought more than a knowledge of medicine and hospital administration to his new post. Besides being a successful businessman, he brought with him a thorough knowledge of community and city planning—a knowledge acquired as the result of serving on the Board of the American Society of

Artist's conception of the new $109 million, 600,000 square foot West Building of the new Methodist Hospital to be completed in 1986. The new structure, which will incorporate state-of-the-art equipment, will house the hospital's centers for cardiovascular, eye, cancer, neuroscience and trauma. To the left of the new hospital is the new doctors' building.

155

Frank P. Loyd, M.D., for many years a member of the Hospital's executive committee and vice-president of Medical Research, became president of Methodist Hospital on April 1, 1981. Under his direction, the hospital's largest and most ambitious building program is now underway.

Methodist Hospital was one of four Indianapolis Organizations sharing a four-way Casper Award for community service in 1984. The prestigious award, given annually by the Community Service Council, was presented to each of the participants for their cooperative community-wide effort designed to detect cancer of the colon in its early stages. The project included distribution of a free Hemoccult kit and a free laboratory test. Shown accepting the Caspers are (l. to r.): David E. Scott and Jane K. Ambro of the Little Red Door; Donna J. Minnick and Dr. William M. Dugan, Jr., Methodist Hospital; Carrie Jackson, WTHR (ch. 13), and Kenneth Simmons, vice-president and corporate operating officer, Peoples Drug Stores. At the extreme right is Joseph M. Areddy, immediate past president of Community Service Council.

Planning Officials for 10 years, serving two terms as president of the prestigious oganization.

Upon assuming his new duties on April 1, 1981, Dr. Lloyd called for a comprehensive review of corporate policies and programs for the 1980s and beyond. The new decade, in his view, called for new approaches and new strategies to meet the changes in the economy and new reimbursement patterns and government regulations as well as decreased charitable support, increased legal liabilities and new sources of hospital competition. In the earlier decades—the 1960s and 1970s—the strategy had been to focus on clinical excellence and the development of Methodist as a single entity. It was a successful formula, but the policy had not been "sufficiently sensitive" to evolving market forces nor threats to Methodist's share of the health care market.

Even more important—and overshadowing corporate needs and organization—was the paramount question of how best Methodist could continue to provide the very best possible health care and at reasonable cost to every man, woman and child in Indianapolis and the central Indiana area. No changes in corporate policy or organization could be made without thoroughly balancing these changes with community needs. Need and management must interlock and both must be geared to Methodist Hospital's continuing commitment to excellence in health care.

Board members and officers, hospital officials, and members of the medical staff studied the problem. Surveys were made and earlier surveys restudied. Hospital statistics were analyzed. Community needs were surveyed. Meetings were held with state and national leaders in the health care field. Consultants were brought in. There were a myriad of complex questions to be asked and answered. Among them: What would be the health care needs of the future? Which services should be targeted for special emphasis? What would be needed in terms of equipment in the rapidly ad-

A $1 Million anonymous gift was given to increase the care provided for heart patients. Dr. Richard Nay and nurse Doris Crawmer check monitor in cardiovascular section. Dr. Nay, a cardiologist, chairs the committee that administers the fund.

vancing fields of medicine, science and technology? What developments in new methods and healing could be reasonably forecast? What were Methodist's strongest areas—areas in which Methodist functioned best and was an acknowledged leader? How best could Methodist's resources be mobilized to provide the best possible health care and continue Methodist's high standards of excellence?

The new study offered solutions. Methodist would, as always, focus on clinical excellence, but it would move in new directions and in new ways to meet the changing times and the specific needs of Central Indiana as well as other sections of the state served by Methodist. The new strategy called for the development of the hospital and its related organizations as a multiple entity, to be vertically

and horizontally integrated. It was a direction, the study said, that would enable Methodist "to respond rapidly and decisively to complex and unpredictable market forces...market forces which promise to cause major structural changes in the hospital industry in the next decade."

Vertical integration was defined as "any diversification into health care services which involves moving closer to the ultimate user of tertiary care hospital services and includes industrial medicine programs serving the needs of employers; medical office buildings serving the needs of specialty physicians; continuing medical education programs serving the needs of referring physicians in outlying areas; and satellite primary health care centers serving the needs of growing suburban populations."

Vertical integration also meant that Methodist would be entering into businesses supplying the resources needed to run the main hospital operation and enabling it to "pursue opportunities to develop medical technologies which will be of use not only to Methodist but the entire industry." As an example of supplying hospital resources the report cited the operation of its own laundry and the training of its own physicians.

On the subject of horizontal integration the study recommended the linkage of "geographically proximate" hospitals through ownership, lease, management contract, consortia, shared services or special purpose affiliations. It could also mean linkage to other forms of in-patient care, such as nursing homes, minimal care hospitals, of half-way psychiatric facilities.

As part of the new strategy, Methodist would put extra emphasis on five areas of the 14 important areas in which the hospital offered health care. None of the other areas would be neglected and they would continue their commitment to excellence, but cancer, cardiovascular, eye, neurological and trauma would be stressed in the new decade.

The five areas of emphasis—each a center of excellence—were areas in which Methodist was a leader and, in most cases, had won national and international recognition for medical and surgical innovations and programs. Logically, they were also areas in which Methodist had the dominant share of the health care market as evidenced by the large number of patients including a high percentage of referrals from outside Marion County. (Newspaper readers need only recall the frequency with which the phrase "...and later transferred to Methodist Hospital" appears in news stories.)

Coincident with the adoption of plans and market strategies for the 1980s, a corporate reorganization was completed in 1983. Approved by the North and South Indiana Conferences of the United Methodist Church in 1982, the reorganization was designed to insulate the United Methodist Church from financial and legal responsibility for the hospital's actions; create a coordinated system of hospital and other health care providers; and spin off "certain functions which were not allowed full reimbursement to the hospital for its services." The new corporate entities and their functions were defined as:

WESLEY MEDICAL CARE, a non-profit company. Formed to create and implement

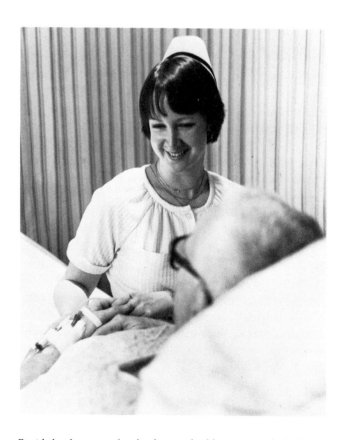

Rapid development of technology in health care must be balanced with greater personal care. Here, Nancy Hedges checks with patient John Hensel.

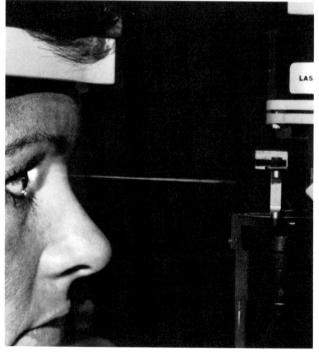

Using the latest technology, the Neodymium YAG laser, ophthalmologists at Methodist Hospital perform eye surgery without incisions, risk of infection, or need to admit the patient to the hospital.

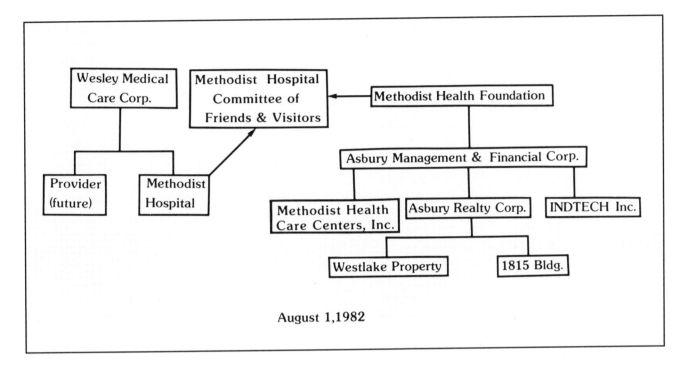

```
Wesley Medical          Methodist Hospital              Methodist Health Foundation
Care Corp.              Committee of              ◄————
                        Friends & Visitors

                                                      Asbury Management & Financial Corp.

  Provider      Methodist
  (future)      Hospital        Methodist Health      Asbury Realty Corp.      INDTECH Inc.
                                Care Centers, Inc.

                                            Westlake Property      1815 Bldg.
```

August 1, 1982

This organizational chart shows the relationship between the two holding companies — Wesley Medical Care Corporation and Methodist Health Foundation — created by the reorganization in 1982. The Committee of Friends and Visitors will help develop resources and support for the immediate and long range future of the hospital and foundation.

a system of affiliated hospitals with Methodist as the major referral center. Eugene M. Busche is Chairman of the Board and Dr. Frank P. Lloyd is president.

METHODIST HEALTH FOUNDATION. In addition to its traditional role as fund raiser for the hospital, the Foundation established a major for-profit entity, Asbury Management and Financial Corporation, to serve as an independent corporation and to operate for-profit health related businesses. Foundation officers are: Eldon Campbell, chairman of the board and president, and Betty Tilson, vice president.

ASBURY MANAGEMENT AND FINANCIAL CORPORATION. As a for-profit subsidiary of the Methodist Health Foundation, the corporation serves as an independent corporation to allocate resources and plan and direct the growth of Methodist Urgent Care Centers, Inc., the Thomas A. Brady Sports Medicine Center, the five Occupational Medicine Centers, the billings and collections divi-

Dedication of the Thomas A. Brady Sports Medicine Center was on September 21, 1983. Above, Eldon Campbell, left, Chairman of the Board and President of the Methodist Health Foundation, congratulates Dr. Brady, a pioneer in sports medicine, in whose honor the center is named. The Asbury Management and Financial Corporation manages the center.

sions, Asbury Realty Corporation, West-lake Development and other properties. President of Asbury is Thomas W. Binford, who succeeded Judith A. Barrett, its first president.

The Asbury Realty Company also finances and develops properties and facilities complementary to the operation of the hospital. Besides ownership of a medical building at 1815 North Capitol and an 18th and Capitol parking garage, it leases four Methodist Hospital Care Centers. The company is presently constructing a medical office building, urgent care center and out-patient surgery on Indianapolis' west side. The new building, to be completed in 1984, is being constructed on 4.4 acres of a 23-acre site formerly occupied by the West Lake Drive-in Theater. Asbury has

also applied for a certificate of need as the first step toward construction of a 180-bed skilled-care nursing home on a five acre site contiguous to the new West-lake Medical Building.

Methodist's major building program, divided into three phases, was designed to emphasize the hospital as an important regional center as well as Methodist Hospital's present and future role. The first phase of the program, construction of an Energy Center, was completed in 1982 on budget and on schedule. Costing $16,000,000, the new facilities structure incorporating 100,000 square feet provides all mechanical, electrical, heating and support systems for the 1,105 bed hospital now and in the future. The building, which replaces the out-dated power house, contains the hospital's power plant, maintenance shops, laundry-linen services, waste disposal (with a heat recovery

The steel framework is in place, upper left and right, for Methodist Hospital's 600,000 square foot West Tower, part of a $152,000,000 building program that will take Methodist into the new century. The Tower will replace about 500 existing surgical, critical care and ob-stetrical beds. Adjoining the tower and seen at the right is the steel structure for a doctor's office building which is being financed independently by a private corporation. The photo was taken in September 1984.

system); bio-medical engineering, environmental services offices, materials handling dock and facilities division offices. Many of the 1,600 people who toured the facility in July were intrigued by a computer-operated laundry system that washed and dried sheets, scrub suits and linens at a rate of 3,000 pounds per hour or 12 tons during an eight-hour shift. Equally amazing to visitors was a heat recovery system which cycled hot air from the laundry dryers to heat the building and recycled hot wash water to preheat the next load's wash water.

Phase II of the building plan involved the purchase of land tracts in the vicinity of the hospital and the closing and redirection of Senate Avenue to make way for the third phase, the construction of a 600,000 square foot West Tower at a cost of $109,000,000. The building, now under construction on a 10-acre site on the hospital's west side, will be joined on the campus by an eight-story doctor's office building financed independently by a private corporation including some members of the hospital's medical staff.

Cited as necessary to update Methodist's facilities in order to continue to serve the health care of Indiana residents and to continue Methodist's enviable record for excellence, the new building will

Workmen raise the final steel beam in topping out ceremony for the new West Building of Methodist Hospital. The topping out beam incorporated the signatures of more than 2,000 Methodist employees.

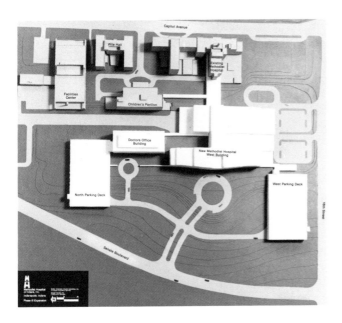

Map shows location of the new Methodist Hospital West Building, Doctors Office Building, and north and west parking decks — all part of the hospital's Phase III expansion plan to be completed in 1986. The map does not show the center and south units.

Methodist Hospital's modern energy center, completed in 1982, houses the main power plant, maintenance shops, laundry and linen services; offices, waste disposal with heat recovery system, Bio-medical engineering, environmental services, materials handling, loading dock and facilities division offices.

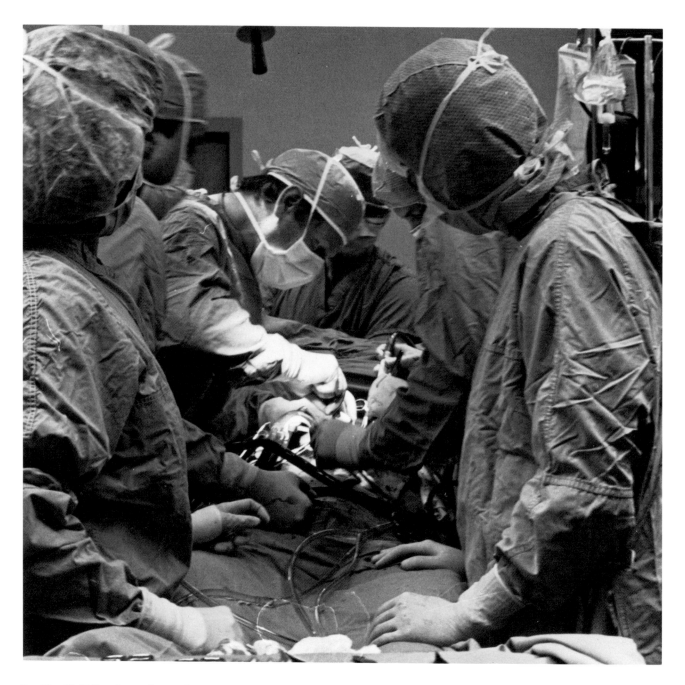

Dr. Harold Halbrook, cardiovascular surgeon, performs a heart transplant operation at Methodist Hospital. Methodist was the first in the Midwest to offer such a procedure and the first to perform the operation in a non-medical school setting. First recipient of a heart transplant was Mrs. Anna Gardner of Crawfordsville, Indiana.

replace about 500 existing surgical, critical care and obstetrical beds. As a result, there will be no increase in the number of beds—now 1,105—but there will be an increase in the number of private or single occupancy rooms.

The five centers of emphasis, defined in the 1981 study, will be housed in the new structure. Eugene Busche, chairman of the hospital's Board of Direc-

tors and president of Indianapolis Life Insurance Company, emphasized that no current services will be eliminated. "Emphasis," he says, "will continue to be placed on improvement of patient care, which is vital to all programs."

Financing for the hospital construction came from many sources including gifts, endowments and from the sale of tax-exempt revenue bonds.

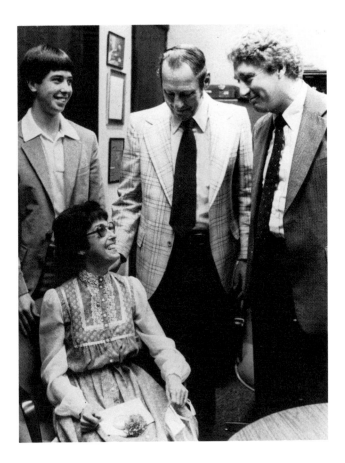

Methodist Hospital's first heart transplant patient, Mrs. Anna Gardner, Crawfordsville, is visited by son, Melvin, left, and husband, Frank, center. At right is cardiologist, Dr. William Storer. The intricate four-hour operation on October 30, 1982 was performed by Dr. Harold Halbrook assisted by a visiting surgeon from Palo Alto, California. It was the first heart transplant to be performed in a non-medical school hospital.

Ruth Lilly, friend of the hospital, daughter of the late J. K. Lilly, Jr., and member of a family that served Methodist Hospital over the years in several capacities, generously contributed $3,000,000 for the new Hospice and Cancer Treatment Center.

Hospital employees donated more than $600,000. Major gifts included a $2,000,000 grant from the Lilly Endowment, Inc., and a $1,500,000 commitment from the Krannert Charitable Trust. Ruth Lilly, daughter of the late J.K. Lilly, Jr. contributed $3,000,000 to the hospital to be applied to building and equipping the new hospice and cancer treatment center. Thomas W. Binford served as general chairman of the Methodist Hospital Capital Gift Campaign. Among several anonymous gifts was one of a $1,000,000 to support the cardiovascular program.

Of the many dramatic medical and surgical developments at Methodist Hospital, perhaps none was more dramatic than the announcement on October 30, 1982 of the first successful heart transplant, the culmination of four years of preparation. The four-hour surgery, performed on

a 38-year-old Crawfordsville resident, Mrs. Anna Gardner, was the first such operation to be performed at a non-medical school hospital. Dr. Harold Halbrook, cardiovascular surgeon, performed the operation assisted by a visiting surgeon from Palo Alto, California.

Mrs. Gardner suffered from cardiomyopathy, a hereditary deterioration of the heart muscle, and doctors had earlier told her she had but a year to live. Placed on the list of possible recipients by her physician, Dr. William Storer, Mrs. Gardner was notified early on the day of the surgery that a donor had become available. Accompanied by her husband, Frank, and son, Melvin, she arrived at the hospital in the afternoon. A self-possessed patient, Mrs. Gardner finished her Christmas shopping from a catalog as she waited in the Cooperative Care Unit.

Mrs. Gardner's transplant was the first of eleven heart transplants to be performed at Methodist during the next 22 months. The surgery was yet

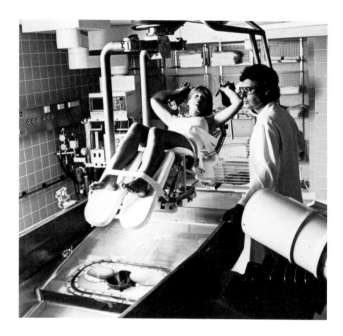

A patient is being lowered into a bath of water to receive treatment by way of the extracorporeal shock wave lithotripter, familiarly known as the kidney stone crusher. The equipment, installed at Methodist Hospital in 1984, pulverizes kidney stones into tiny particles without damaging the surrounding tissue. The particles, reduced to the size of sand or gravel, are excreted in the urine.

Thomas W. Binford, Chairman of the Board and Chief Executive Officer of Indiana National Corporation, served as general campaign chairman for Methodist Hospital's $12 million fund drive to finance a long range facilities plan. Mr. Binford is known as "Mr. Indianapolis" by virtue of his long civic and corporate achievements.

another example of the progressiveness of the hospital's cardiovascular unit which continues to be one of the most extensive cardiac programs in Indiana.

To further its commitment to excellence, Methodist installed new equipment to diagnose and treat patients. A new ultrasound machine was installed for early detection of breast cancer and another computerized tomography scanner was installed in a van to provide service to outlying hospitals. Mark Singer, M.D., and Eric Blom, Ph.D., developed the Blom-Singer Voice Prosthesis for victims of laryngectomies. For the first time patients who had undergone surgery for a cancerous larynx were able to talk almost normally.

In 1984 Methodist installed an extracorporeal shock wave lithotripter, a device that pulverizes kidney stones with acoustic shock waves thus precluding the need for surgery. The $2,000,000 machine uses an X-ray to locate the kidney stone and then focuses on the stone and pulverizes it with shock waves. The particles, the size of sand or gravel, are then excreted in the urine. Patients using the treatment require a four-day hospital stay as compared to surgical patients who require five to fifteen days hospitalization, followed by four to six weeks of convalescence. Developed in Germany the lithotripter was the first to be used in the United States. The Food and Drug Administration is supervising the testing of the machine with selected patients.

The White Cross Guild marked its 50th birthday in its new home at 1500 Stadium Drive where it had moved the year before. The former Service Center, built in 1944, was torn down and the fireplace motto removed to the new structure. The stones from the fireplace were sold as mementos for $2 each. White Cross Guild volunteers manned switchboards for another Methodist Hospital innovation, Call for Health, a personal telephone information service that provides free doctor approved answers to questions on health and wellness. An educational service of the hospital, the

Dr. Richard Nay   Ardath Burkhart   Francis Hughes

Three who cared: Dr. Richard Nay, the late Ardath Burkhart, and Francis Hughes. Dr. Nay, who joined Methodist Hospital's staff in 1947 and was the first physician to be elected to the Board of Directors, headed fund raising efforts among physicians during the $12 million capital campaign. Mrs. Burkhart, long a friend of the hospital and a long time member of the Methodist Hospital Foundation, served as vice-president for the capital campaign. Mr. Hughes, who headed the capital solicitation from the Board and Foundation members, was chairman of the Hospital Board of Trustees for two terms. He retired in 1982 as Chairman of the Methodist Hospital Foundation after serving for 20 years. All three were honored for their work at a dinner on October 19, 1983 attended by more than 600 friends and guests. They will be honored further in three sections of the hospital's new construction program. A sculpture court between the West Tower and B Building will be named after Mrs. Burkhart; the new Board Room will be named for Mr. Hughes and the new coronary care unit will be named for Dr. Nay.

Call for Health library contains 200 tapes dealing with 27 different subjects ranging from arthritis to venereal disease.

Methodist Hospital, now 85 years of age and looking toward its first century of service, is a medical complex of 1105 beds, 4584 employees, 835 doctors. It covers 35 acres with its land and buildings valued at $108,146,000. Nationally recognized for its excellent care and progress in medicine and surgery, it ranks 17th among United States hospitals in bed capacity.

Not unlike many other American institutions, Methodist Hospital began as an idea, nutured by need, and funded by a few thousand dollars. Over the years it grew and survived and went on to new heights of achievement despite war and depressions, social upheavals and economic changes. Its success can be attributed to many factors but perhaps the most important has been the thousands of people who kept that early dream alive and so generously contributed their time and money to create a great hospital that serves all people. In turn, Methodist has remained not only committed to compassionate health care, but it has continued to be "a blessed ministry."

Perhaps Dr. Frank P. Lloyd, president of Methodist Hospital, said it best in a recent interview:

"Methodist Hospital," he said, "is more than a place of healing. Methodist has a commitment to provide the very best in health care, compassion in its delivery, devotion to its patients and dedication to the God we serve."

Appendix A

Acknowledgments

This book was made possible only because of the many valuable contributions of scores of individuals and organizations. The authors are especially indebted to Marjorie K. Woods, Administrative Assistant for Church Relations, Methodist Hospital, who served many functions from researcher to typist for the project. She spent long hours over and above the call of duty in digging out elusive facts and verifying others while drawing upon her many years of service at Methodist Hospital in preparing material for review.

Others who provided valuable assistance include David Richard and staff, Office of Corporate Communications; David Willoughby and staff, Medical Media Productions; Ms. Patricia Belding and staff, Medical Staff Office; the staff of the Methodist Hospital Library with special thanks to Lois Clark, librarian; Preston Huff and staff, Records Management and Hospital Archives; DePauw University Library, Archives of Methodist Church in Indiana, with special thanks to Virginia C. Brand.

Also, Ms. Sandra Fitzgerald and Charlesetta Means of *The Indianapolis Star* and *The Indianapolis News* library; Marion County Medical Society, Hal Hafner and staff; Indianapolis-Marion County Public Library; Indiana State Library, Indiana Section; Library, Indiana University School of Medicine; Indiana Historical Society, Medical History Section, Charles A. Bonsett, M.D., chairman; Ann G. Carmichael, M.D., medical historian consultant, *The Indiana Medical History Quarterly* and assistant professor, Indiana University Department, History of Philosophy and Science; Katherine Mandusie McDonell, managing editor, *The Indiana Medical History Quarterly;* Mr. Martin Badger, editor, *Journal of Indiana Medicine,* Indiana State Medical Association; Betty Buchanan, volunteer researcher; Jack A.L. Hahn, retired president of Methodist Hospital.

Elizabeth A. Duvall, R.N. Nursing Department (retired) provided invaluable assistance in providing a history of nursing. And special thanks are due all officers, department heads and employees of Methodist Hospital who provided not only wholehearted cooperation but furnished pictures and information.

Special thanks also to the 25 employees, physicians and Board members, present and retired, who read the manuscript in its final stages of preparation and made substantive contribution to its development.

Appendix B

Sources/Bibliography

Interviews

Daniel F. Evans and Francis M. Hughes, former presidents of the Board of Trustees; Mrs. John H. Warvel, Sr., R.N., retired; Dr. John H. Warvel, Jr.; Jack A.L. Hahn, retired president, Methodist Hospital; Mrs. Barbara (Webb) Hahn, R.N., retired; Fredericka Koch, R.N., retired, former director of Nursing and Nurses Training School; Dr. Edward F. Bloemker, retired chief of Anesthesiology and former president of The Medical Staff; Dr. Lester H. Hoyt, retired director of Clinical Pathology Laboratories.

Also, Mrs. Katherine Brewer Pattison, R.N., retired, graduate of first School of Nursing class; Dr. Jack H. Hall, former vice president, Medical Education; Dr. Hugh K. Thatcher, past president, Medical Staff; Dr. Harold C. Oschner, retired, director Radiology; Dr. Thomas A. Brady; Dr. Stephen J. Jay, vice president, Academic Affairs; Dr. Hunter A. Soper, vice president, Medical Affairs; Dr. Bernard D. Rosenak, member Medical History Section of Indiana Historical Society; Dr. J. Kenneth Forbes, executive assistant to bishop and member of the Board of Directors; Joseph E. Aufderheide, retired, chief of Pharmacy; Mr. Robert H. Suckow, retired, director of Public Relations and Development; Mrs. Spurling Clark; Dr. Frank P. Lloyd, president of Methodist Hospital; and many other physicians and employees, present and retired, who provided information and clarification of many of the details contained in this history.

Publications

General

Annual Conference Minutes, the Indiana, Northwest Indiana and North Indiana Annual Conferences for 1890 and selected years.

Ayling, Stanley, *John Wesley*, Abingdon Press, Nashville, 1979

The Indiana Medical History Quarterly, "Indiana Central Medical College," Indianapolis, Indiana Historical Society, Vol. VIII, No. 4, 1982

Heller, Herbert L., *The Indiana Conference of the Methodist Church: 1832-1956*, Historical Society of Indiana Conference, 1957.

Hill, A, Wesley, *John Wesley Among the Physicians*, London, The Epworth Press, 1956.

Holloway, W.R., "Indianapolis Railroad City," *Indianapolis Journal*, 1870

Indianapolis City Almanacs, selected years.

Leary, Edward A., *Indianapolis, the Story of a City*, Indianapolis, the Bobbs-Merrill Company, 1970.

Parkinson, George H. Unpublished *History of Methodist Board of Hospital and Homes*, 1954.

Patten, H.B., Robertson, L.A., *A History of the Indianapolis Epworth League*, 1891-1907.

Russo, Dorothy Ritter, Editor-in-chief, *One Hundred Years of Indiana Medicine*, Indiana Historical Society, 1949. Published in connection with Centennial of the Indiana State Medical Association and prepared under the direction of Charles M. Combs, M.D., and Edgar F. Kiser, M.D.

Silver Anniversary Record Book, Indianapolis, Indians, Indianapolis, 1980.

The Book of Discipline of the Methodist Episcopal Church, 1900 and selected editions.

Urdang, Lawrence, editor, *The Timetables of American History*, New York, Simon and Schuster, 1981.

Walsh, William H., M.D., *The Hospitals of Indianapolis: A Survey*, Indianapolis Foundation, 1928.

Wesley, John *Primitive Physik*, 22nd edition, Parry Hall, Philadelphia, 1791.

Publications (continued)

Methodist Hospital

Editions of *The Good Samaritan, Methodist Hospital News* and the hospital's *The Beacon.* Also, Year Books of the School of Nursing and a long list of pamphlets, booklets, brochures and programs including those of the Methodist Hospital Foundation. Of special help was the unpublished manuscript, *A History of Methodist Hospital,* by the Reverend Dr. C.T. Alexander, former chaplain, updated by Florence Stone and Bea Northcott, formerly of the hospital's public relations department.

Newspapers

The Indianapolis Star, The Indianapolis News, The Indianapolis Times, The Western Christian Advocate, and the *Hoosier United Methodist.* We are indebted to the clipping service of the Social Service Department of the Marion County Public Library as well as the newspaper index section of the Indiana Division of the Indiana State Library.

Hospital Records

Minutes of the Board of Trustees; reports of hospital superintendents; reports of the superintendent of nurses, minutes and reports of the Medical Staff, Methodist Hospital, and corporate documents.

Appendix C

Presidents/Chairmen
Methodist Hospital Board of Trustees

Leslie J. Naftzger
President
1900

E. B. Rawls
President
1901

Charles E. Bacon
President
1901 - 1908

W. C. Van Arsdel
President
1908 - 1910
1918 - 1921

Charles W. Fairbanks
President
1910 - 1918

Arthur V. Brown
President
1922 - 1942

Titus Lowe
President
1942 - 1948

William B. Schiltges
President
1948 - 1955

William G. Davis
President
1955 - 1958

Arthur G. Wilson
President
1958 - 1961

Francis M. Hughes
President
1961 - 1965

Daniel F. Evans
President
1965 - 1968

H. Prentice Browning
President
1968 - 1969

Alex L. Taggart III
Chairman
1969 - 1970

Russell R. Hirschman
Chairman
1970 - 1973

Lester G. Irons
Chairman
1973 - 1976

Eldon Campbell
Chairman
1976 - 1979

Alvin Kuehn
Chairman
1979 - 1982

Eugene Busche
Chairman
1982 -

Appendix D

Superintendents/Presidents
Methodist Hospital of Indiana, Inc.

Marilla Williams, Deaconess
1908-1909

W.T. Graham, M.D.
1909-1911

J.M. Moulder, M.D.
1912-1914

Charles S. Woods, M.D.
1915-1922

Demetrious Tillotson D.D.
1922-1923

George M. Smith, D.D.
1923-1931

John G. Benson, D.D.
1931-1944

Orien Fifer, D.D. (Acting)
1944

Robert E. Neff, L L.D.
1945-1954

Jack A.L. Hahn, L L.D.
1955-1981

Frank P. Lloyd, M.D.
1981-

Appendix E

Presforms of the Medical Staff
of Methodist Hospital of Indiana, Inc.

Excerpts from a History of Methodist Hospital

June 18, 1920, was a significant date in the hospital's history. On that day, fifty-seven physicians met to form the progenitor of the Medical Staff. They were not then permitted to use the word "staff", so we find the term "Clinical Research Society" applied to the group, with Dr. Murray N. Hadley as Chairman. The purpose was to increase hospital efficiency and improve the professional attainments of its members. The self-approved constitution and by-laws were adopted on July 13, 1920. Physicians outside the city were admitted to Society Membership on May 5, 1922.

The first regular scientific meeting was called to order by Dr. Murray N. Hadley on September 3, 1920, Dr. Homer G. Hamer, Secretary. Drs. A.C. Kimberlin, John A. MacDonald, Ernest DeWolfe Wales and Edgar F. Kiser were the first Executive Committee. Dr. C.S. Woods, Superintendent, addressed the group on the standardization of hospitals, staff organizations, meetings and action on fee splitting. The members present dutifully agreed to cooperate in every way that it might be possible for the hospital to conform to the minimum requirements. At the time of that first meeting there were eighty-seven names on the roster. A

call was made for new applications for membership, none received; an incident which has hardly occurred since.

Murray W. Hadley, M.D.
1921-22

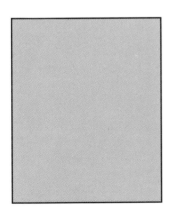

R.C. Ottinger, M.D.
1923

Homer G. Hamer, M.D.
1924

Charles N. Sowders, M.D.
1925

Charles Cabalzer, M.D.
1926

Robert M. Moore, M.D.
1927

Henry O. Mertz, M.D.
1928

John H. Eberwein, M.D.
1929

Rollin H. Moser, M.D.
1930

Joseph W. Ricketts, M.D.
1931

John W. Carmack, M.D.
1932

LaRue D. Carter, M.D.
1933

James O. Ritchey, M.D.
1934

Carl H. McCaskey, M.D.
1935

Ernest O. Asher, M.D.
1936

Cleon Nafe, M.D.
1937

Walter P. Morton, M.D.
1938-39

William N. Wishard, M.D.
1940

Foster J. Hudson, M.D.
1941

Harry L. Foreman, M.D.
1942

John Whitehead, M.D.
1943

Harry R. Kerr, M.D.
1944

Norman S. Loomis, M.D.
1945

William M. Dugan, M.D.
1946

Roy A. Geider, M.D.
1947

Charles F. Thompson, M.D.
1948

James W. Denny, M.D.
1949

William E. Gabe, M.D.
1950

Edward F. Bloemker, M.D.
1951

Robert D. Howell, M.D.
1952

Ralph V. Everly, M.D.
1953

E. Vernon Hahn, M.D.

1954

Arthur N. Jay, M.D.

1955

Paul K. Cullen, M.D.

1956-57

Earl W. Mericle, M.D.

1958

Gordon W. Batman, M.D.

1959-60

Lawson J. Clark, M.D.

1961-62

Glen V. Ryan, M.D.

1963

Louis W. Nie, M.D.

1964-65

Arnold J. Bachmann, M.D.

1966-67

Donald E. Stephens, M.D.
1968-69

John H.O. Mertz, M.D.
1970-71

Warren E. Coggeshall, M.D.
1972-73

Hugh K. Thatcher, M.D.
1974-75

Donald L. Rogers, M.D.
1976-77

James H. Gosman, M.D.
1978-79

Hunter A. Soper, M.D.
1980-81

Daniel M. Newman, M.D.
1982-83

John G. Pantzer, Jr., M.D.
1984

Appendix F

Charter Members of the Methodist Hospital Clinical Research Society   July 13, 1920

Name	Address	Classification
Abbett, Frank E.	608 Hume-Mansur Bl.	Obstetrics & Gyn.
Alburger, Henry R.	403 Hume-Mansur Bl.	Internal Med.
Bannister, Revel F.	2958 Central Ave.	Abd. & Gen. Surg.
Barnhill, John F.	408 Pennway Bl.	Surgery
Beckman, H.F.	514 Hume-Mansur Bl.	Obstetrics
Beeler, Raymond C.	712 Hume-Mansur Bl.	Roentgenology
Best, William P.	610 Bankers Trust Bl.	General
Bonn, H.K.	201 Pennway Bl.	Gen. Abd. & G.U. Surg.
Cabalzer, Charles	508 Hume-Mansur Bl.	Anaesthesia & Surg.
Carmack, John W.	37 Willoughby Bl.	Ear, Nose & Throat
Clark, Edmund D.	712 Hume-Mansur Bl.	Surgery
Cofield, Ernest D., DDS	314 Bd. of Trade Bl.	Extractomy
Cunningham, John M.	508 Hume-Mansur Bl.	
Day, Clark E.	740 Bankers Trust Bl.	Gyn, Med. & Obstetrics
Doepper, William A.	610 Hume-Mansur Bl.	Anaesthesia
Earp, S.E.	634 Occidental Bl	Medicine
Eberwein, John H.	720 Hume-Mansur Bl.	Abd. & Gen. Surg.
Egbert, James	226 Bankers Trust Bl.	Ear, Nose & Throat
Egart, Stephen L.	468 Blake St.	Gen. Medicine
Erdman, Bernard	27 Willoughby Bl.	Genito-Urinary
Ferguson, Charles E.	412 E. 17th St.	Obstetrics
Foxworthy, Frank W.	1135 State Life Bl.	Gastro-Intes. & Rect.
Gabe, William E.	712 Hume-Mansur Bl.	Surgery
Gilchrist, E.S., DDS	417 E. 16th St.	
Graham, A.B.	30 Willoughby Bl.	Gastro-Intestinal
Hadley, M.N.	608 Hume-Mansur Bldg.	Gen. & Abd. Surg.
Haggard, E.M.	529 Bankers Trust Bl.	
Hamer, H.G.	723 Hume-Mansur Bl.	Genito-Urinary
Hatfield, Sidney J.	409 Odd Fellows Bl.	Gyn. & Abd. Surg.
Heinrichs, H.H.	740 Bankers Trust Bl.	
Hetherington, A.M.	718 Hume-Mansur Bl.	Surg. & Obstetrics
Holman, Jerome E.	3315 E. 10th St.	Surg. & Obstetrics
Hughes, W.F.	401 Hume-Mansur Bl.	Eye
Humes, C.D.	707 Hume-Mansur Bl.	Neurology
Jackson, G.B.	603 Hume-Mansur Bl.	Gyn. & Obstetrics
Jaeger, A.S.	429 Bankers Trust Bl.	Gyn. & Abd. Surg.
Kahn, D.L.	128 East 22nd St.	
Kast, Marie	M.E. Hospital	Anaesthetist
Kearby, D.O.	422 Am. Cent. Life Bl.	Ear, Nose & Throat

Name	Address	Classification
Ketcham, Jane	514 Hume-Mansur Bl.	O.B.
Kimberlin, A.C.	57 Willoughby Bl.	Medicine
Kiser, Edgar F.	226 Hume-Mansur Bl.	Med.
Kohlstaedt, Geo. W.	2174 Madison Ave.	Radium.
Leasure, J. Kent	422 Am. Cent. Life Bl.	Ear, Nose & Throat
Light, Mason	924 East 63rd St.	A.L.R.
Link, Goethe	606 Ind. Pythian Bl.	Surgery
Marlatt, Clarence L.	700 Kahn Bl.	General
Masters, Robert J.	422 Hume-Mansur Bl.	Gen. Medicine
Mertz, H.O.	723 Hume-Mansur Bl.	Urology
Milliken, Robert R.	613 Hume-Mansur Bl.	Surgery
Molt, W.F.	529 Bankers Trust Bl.	Ear, Nose & Throat
Moore, Robert M.	521 Hume-Mansur Bl.	Int. Med.
Mueller, Lillian	422 Am. Cent. Life Bl.	Ear, Nose & Throat
Moschelle, J.D.	901 Odd Fellows Bl.	Surgery
Mozingo, A.E.	720 K. of P. Bl.	Empyema
Mumford, E.B.	408 Hume-Mansur Bl.	Orthopedic Surg.
McAlexander, R.O.	740 Bankers Trust Bl.	Gen. & Abd. Surg.
McCaskey, C.H.	422 Am. Cent. Life Bl.	Ear, Nose & Throat
McCown, P.E.	520 Hume-Mansur Bl.	Urology
McCulloch, Carleton B.	1135 State Life Bl.	Surgery
MacDonald, John A.	408 Hume-Mansur Bl.	Internal Med.
New, C.F.	1011 N. Pennsylvania St.	Neurology
Orders, D.E.	350 Bankers Trust Bl.	
Ottinger, R.C.	508 Hume-Mansur Bl.	Gyn. & Abd. Surg.
Overman, F.V.	508 Hume-Mansur Bl.	Ear, Nose & Throat
Pantzer, Hugo		Surgery
Padgett, E.E.	424 Hume-Mansur Bl.	Abd. & Gen. Surg.
Pfafflin, Charles A.	445 Bankers Trust Bl.	Opthalmology
Reed, Jewett V.	613 Hume-Mansur Bl.	Gen. & Abd. Surg.
Repass, R.E.	702 Hume-Mansur Bl.	Ear, Nose & Throat
Ridgway, O.W.	417 E. 16th St.	Surgery
Rogers, Clarke	624 Hume-Mansur Bl.	Internal Med.
Ross, David	416 Bd. of Trade Bl.	Surgery
Seaton, G.W.	620 Bankers Trust Bl.	Ear, Nose & throat
Segar, Louis H.	226 Hume-Mansur Bl.	Pediatrics
Smith, Roy Lee	720 K. Of P. Bl.	Genito-Urinary
Sowders, Charles R.	408 Pennway Bl.	Internal Med.
Strickland, Clarence R.	331 N. Delaware St.	Internal Med.
Thurston, A.L.	57 Willoughby Bl.	Internal Med.
Torian, O.N.	620 Hume-Mansur Bl.	Pediatrics & Obstetrics
VanOsdol, H.A.	314 Bd. of Trade Bl.	Ear, Nose & Throat
Wales, E. DeW.	620 Hume-Mansur Bl.	Ear, Nose & Throat
Walker, F.C.	414 Hume-Mansur Bl.	Surgery
Wheeler, H.H.	311 Hume-Mansur Bl.	Gastro-Intestinal
Williams, Luther	232 Hume-Mansur Bl.	Gen. & Abd. Surg.
Wishard, W.N.	723 Hume-Mansur Bl.	Genito-Urinary
Woods, C.S.	M.E. Hospital	Int. Med. & Supt. M.E. Hosp.

Appendix G

Superintendents/Directors of Nursing and School of Nursing

Originally, the superintendent of nurses also served as head of the School of Nursing with the title, Principal of the School of Nursing and Superintendent of Nurses or vice versa. During the tenure of Miss Hazel B. Whittern, 1944-1946, the title was changed to Director of Nursing and School of Nursing. Following the closure of the nursing school in 1968, the title became Director of Nursing. In response to a proposal from Hospital Administration in 1977 to disband the Nursing Services, nursing administrative staff recommended that the Nursing Department have its own administrative head and the title Vice President of Nursing. Upon the appointment of Mrs. Susan Sheedy, December 18, 1978, the title was changed. In May 1981, following a major reorganization of the hospital administration, the title was changed to Vice President, Operations, for Nursing and Patient Support Services with responsibility for the Nursing Service, Nutrition and Dietetics Department, Environmental Services and Patient Transportation.

Those who served as head of the Nursing Department and School of Nursing, etc., were as follows:

Principals of the School of Nursing and Superintendents of Nurses

Miss Goldsmith, Deaconness, R.N.
1908 (a few months)

Miss Margaret Lehman, R.N.
1908-1909

Miss Lena Salmon, R.N.
1909-1910

Miss Julia Adams, R.N.
1910-1911

Miss Jessie Horn, R.N.
1911-1914

Miss Rebecca Galt, R.N.
1914-1916

Miss Frances Marsh, R.N.
1916-1917

Miss June Gray, R.N.
1917-1918

Miss Edith Mitch, R.N.
1918-1920

Miss Fannie Paine, R.N.
1920-1924

Miss Frances McMillian, R.N.
1924-1932

Miss Grace L. Gray, R.N.,
B.S., M.S.
1932-1933

Miss Fannie Forth, R.N.
1933-1935

Miss Orpha Kendall, R.N.
1936-1939

Miss Bertha L. Pullen, R.N.,
B.S., M.A.
1939-1944

Directors of Nursing and School of Nursing

Miss Hazel B. Whittern, R.N.,
B.S., M.A.
1944-1946

Miss E. Louise Grant, R.N.,
B.S., M.A.
1946-1950

Miss Fredericka E. Koch, R.N.,
B.S., M.A.
1950-1971

Directors of Nursing

Mrs. Ruth Longere Parke, R.N.,
B.S., M.S.
1971-1977

Mrs. Eileen Ely, R.N.,
B.S., M.S.
(Acting Director)
1977-1978

Vice President, Operations for Nursing and Patient Support Services

Mrs. Susan Sheedy, R.N., B.S.N.,
M.S., P.H., H.S.A.
1978-1982

Mrs. Judith A. Barrett, R.N.
1983-

Appendix H

Original Members of the Methodist Hospital Guild 1912 Roster

Mrs. H.C. Allen
Mrs. E. Branham
Miss Eliza Browning
Mrs. A.J. Beveridge
Dr. C.E. Bacon
Mrs. C.E. Bacon
Mrs. W.B. Burforn
Mrs. Billiter
Mrs. Harry Chapman
Mrs. George W. Clelland
Mrs. A.C. Cost
Mrs. Harry Caylor
Mrs. J.M. Dalrymple
Miss K. Dunn
Mrs. H.R. Danner
Mrs. Donaldson
Mrs. Evans
Mrs. E. Easton
Mrs. J.D. Ely
Mrs. M.D. Foxworthy
Mrs. C.W. Fairbanks
Mrs. C.M. Griffin
Miss May Gorby

Mrs. W.M. Gates
Mrs. A.C. Hawn
Mrs. George Henninger
Mrs. E.G. Hunt
Mrs. Hudgins
Mrs. Juliett Herriot
Mrs. Ida A. Harris
Mrs. F.B. Kiser
Mrs. Edgar Kiser
Mrs. J.H. King
Mrs. V.A. Longaker
Mrs. Waller Marmon
Dr. McKenzie
Mrs. W.E. McKenzie
Mrs. Lucy Moulder
Dr. McLean Moulder
Mrs. McClosky
Mrs. W.K. Milholland
Mrs. M.E. McCormick
Mrs. B. Maxwell
Mrs. Pruitt
Mrs. L.A. Robertson
Mrs. R.B. Rudy

Mrs. E.E. Robert
Miss Alla Roberts
Mrs. Charles Railsback
Mrs. W.B. Robertson
Miss Blanche Robinson
Mrs. George Snowden
Mrs. H. Schlotzhauer
Miss Leo Stephenson
Mrs. Daniel Stewart
Mrs. M. Swadener
Mr. R.O. Sneldon
Miss B. Samuels
Mrs. J. Standfield
Mrs. Stint
Mrs. J. Shafer
Mrs. Joseph Stout
Miss Anne Seybord
Miss Gertrude Taggart
Mrs. Elizabeth Taylor
Miss Nell Van Bergen
Mrs. Yontz

Appendix I

Presidents of the White Cross Guild

Mrs. Edgar Blake
Feb. 1932-May 1932

Louella McWhirter
(Mrs. Felix)
1932-1934

Lulu M. Hartinger
(Mrs. William C.)
1934-1936

Bertha Born
(Mrs. Isaac)
1936-1938

Maud Noble
(Mrs. John W.)
1938-1940

Maude L. Ploch
(Mrs. C.A.)
1940-1942

Iona Jay Foreman
(Mrs. Harry L.)
1942-1944

Myrtle L. Bartley
(Mrs. D.A.)
1944-1946

Esther W. Crooks
(Mrs. James)
1946-1948

Esther M. Fairbanks
(Mrs. Arthur A.)
1948-1950

Lillian A. Krause
(Mrs. Harry W.)
1950-1952

Ruth Stuart
(Mrs. James A.)
1952-1954

Vella Harper
(Mrs. R. Dwight)
1954-1956

Mrs. John K. Garriott
1956-1958

Mrs. F.E. Thornburgh
1958-1960

Mrs. W.H. Fortney
1960-1961

Mrs. John D. Greenlee
1961-1963

**June Swiggett
(Mrs. Herbert)**
1963-1965

**Mildred Wacker
(Mrs. Jerome)**
1965-1967

**Annice Bernhardt
(Mrs. Edward)**
1967-1969

**Mary Readle
(Mrs. Edwin)**
1969-1971

Mrs. Bryce Bottom
1971-1973

Mrs. James Perkins
1973-1975

Mrs. Charles Barnes
1975-1977

Mrs. Grover Streepy
1977-1979

Mrs. Donald McWhorter
1979-1981

Mrs. Agnes Spencer
May 6, 1981-May 8, 1981

Mrs. Clyde Haine
1981-1983

Mrs. Vera Bray
(Mrs. Gurney)
1983-

Appendix J

Employees of the Year

1964	Emma Beaver	Admitting
1965	Mae Blush Millett	Nursing
1966	Clarence Johnson	Lab
1967	Lovetta Russell	Nursing
1968	Raymond Lanham	Chaplaincy
1969	John Hurt	Physical Therapy
1970	Joe Lyons	Pharmacy
1971	Fred Martin	Environmental Services
1972	Lena Bailey	Finance
1973	Mary Hurt	Mail Room
1974	Wilma Boger	Central Services
1975	Dr. Lester Hoyt	Lab
1976	John Lloyd	Blood Bank
1977	Perry Bereman	Credit Union
1978	Odessa Thomas	O.R. Services
1979	Joan Sechman	Copy Center
1980	Oliver Rawls	Environmental Services
1981	Leota Alexander	Personnel Services
1982	Richard Bailey	Chaplaincy
1983	BeEthel Walker	Surgical Nursing
1984	George Harris	Clinical Laboratories

Appendix K

Boards of Directors

Board of Directors
Methodist Health Foundation
1984-85

Reverend Benjamin Antle
Trinity United Methodist Church

Dale S. Benson, M.D.
Director, Ambulatory Services
Methodist Hospital of Indiana, Inc.

Eugene Busche,
President
Indianapolis Life Insurance Company

Eldon Campbell
President and Chairman
Methodist Health Foundation, Inc.

Alex S. Carroll
Senior Vice President
Thomson McKinnon Securities, Inc.

John Coldren,
Attorney

Reverend Harry Coleman
University United Methodist Church

Reverend Charles Ellinwood
Superintendent, Muncie District
The United Methodist Church

Dr. J. Kenneth Forbes
Executive Assistant
Indiana Area, United Methodist Church

Sam H. Jones,
President
Indianapolis Urban League, Inc.

Frank P. Lloyd, M.D.,
President
Methodist Hospital of Indiana, Inc.

Harold C. McCarthy,
President
Meridian Mutual Insurance Company

Reverend Samuel B. Phillips,
Superintendent
West Indianapolis District
United Methodist Church

Marjorie C. Tarplee,
Executive Director
Central Newspapers Foundation

Mrs. Harry Weaver, Jr.
Housewife

Index